MIND'S EYE

OF

RICHARD BUCKMINSTER FULLER

Embryo of Fuller's One-ocean World map projection patent

MIND'S EYE

OF

RICHARD

BUCKMINSTER FULLER

by

DONALD W. ROBERTSON

St. Martin's Press
New York

Library of Congress Cataloging in Publication Data

Robertson, Donald W.
  The mind's eye of Buckminster Fuller.

  Reprint. Originally published: The mind's eye of
Richard Buckminster Fuller. 1st ed. New York: Vantage
Press, 1974.
  Includes bibliographical references.
  1. Fuller, R. Buckminster (Richard Buckminster),
1895-1983. 2. Inventors—United States—Biography.
I. Title.
[TA140.F9R56 1983]   620'.00092'4 [B]   83-10917
ISBN 0-312-53346-2

First published in 1974 by Vantage Press, Inc.

10 9 8 7 6 5 4 3 2 1

PREFACE

FOR the chronology of the patented Fuller inventions, the author has chosen to use the official filing dates from the records of the United States Patent Office. It will be appreciated that the dates of conception in each case would be somewhat earlier, and that the length of time between concept and filing of the application for patent is a variable, so that the inventions would not necessarily have been made in the same sequence that the filing dates would suggest. Yet with only one unimportant exception, the official dates do fall in the same order as the dates of conception and reduction to practice. Hence it seems best to use only the official dates that are fixed with certainty by the public records.

No exact date is fixed for Fuller's Energetic and Synergetic Geometry, for this was evolved over a quarter of a century. Where quotations are given from a typical classroom teaching session, such are taken from the privately published "preliminary fragment" of the geometry, the author's copy of which bears date of November 9, 1955.* An earlier document, entitled Dymaxion Comprehensive System—Introducing Energetic Geometry, is dated March 14, 1944.* As the latter date precedes the December, 1951, filing date for the first patent in geodesics, the earliest of the inventions to be analyzed in this study, it will be seen that the fundamentals of the geometry were discovered before any of these particular inventions came into the Patent Office. Thus it is that the fabric of the inventor's comprehensive approach to geometry will be found to be inextricably woven into the compatible fabric of the several inventions.

---

*Copyright of the same year

The inventions selected for study include the one represented by the primary geodesics patent, and all of those which followed. These were not all of Fuller's inventions, as they were preceded by a number of others, including patents relating to tensile stress values in houses made of preformed components. This earlier group of patents has been omitted in order to focus on the uniquely related discoveries and inventions in geometry, cartography, architecture and undersea islands.

The second and third paragraphs of the epilogue, written in Fuller's own hand, first appeared as part of an exposition on Tensegrity prepared for Portfolio and Art News Annual, 1961, and are reproduced by permission.

In addition to reliance on the documentary sources cited, the author has drawn upon the knowledge and "feel" of Fuller's thought patterns gained through a rewarding twenty-five years of service as his patent lawyer. For his was the challenging and exciting task of capturing the fullest outreach of Fuller's discoveries for the examiners and readers of patents.

Donald W. Robertson

Ajijic, Jalisco, Mexico
November 1, 1972

They asked, "Why houses in the round?"
Why make them square? said he.

But more, why tie your thoughts at all,
To round, or square. Or old geometry,
That's dead and strange to all reality.

For Universe is life and motion.
There's more of form and energy
Than of material things we see.

We must think comprehensively.

CONTENTS

MIND'S EYE
OF
RICHARD BUCKMINSTER FULLER

Chapter 1

REALITY OF THE UNSEEN

MAN, in unending pursuit of a more complete understanding of the universe, has developed the fabric of his thought mainly by searching out particular truths and then endeavoring to fit these together. In this piecemeal fashion, he has striven for better understanding of the whole. Out of the infinite number of ways in which the fragments of truth can be put together, through eons of patient thought he one day produces—quite by accident—the discovery of some more comprehensive whole, and understanding grows concerning the real meaning of the beginning fragments. This kind of breakthrough he is accustomed to think of as "discovery" or "invention."

Richard Buckminster Fuller, born[1] to test every preconceived notion, and to reject every "can't do" of man, possesses the rare faculty of being able to subjugate the truth fragments of old knowledge while he gains wider perspective through contemplation of what he calls "the totality of a problem." He, pursuing this less tramelled approach, has been the tutor and mentor of the excited imaginations of student, scholar and thinker among all peoples, bringing to them the surging power of fresh, unimpeded thought patterns.

The inspiration of Fuller's teaching has brought personal tribute in the form of widespread comment in the public prints round the world. During four decades, 1928-1968, the

---

[1]July 12, 1895, at Milton, Massachusetts

number of original published items concerning his discoveries and teaching probably transcends that relating to any other leader of thought, heads of state excepted.[2]

The notices and accolades have been written. Fuller's biographers have furnished more critical appraisal of the man's life, inventions and philosophy. It is more the purpose of the work at hand to examine analytically the characteristics of Fuller's mind as it has driven its creative distances into new regions of mathematics and invention. We will do this through consideration of the fundamentals of Fuller's new geometry and of his patented inventions.[3]

Now in the last third of century twenty, man's intellect has grown increasingly aware of the unseen. From early school days we have understood the reality of electricity unseen and invisible although clearly visible in its effects. The light it makes can be seen, the heat felt and the muscle power of the electric motor in lightening physical burdens appreciated. Awareness of the unseen, heightened by what have long since become the commonplaces of radio and television, has been translated in our minds to realization that unseen phenomena are a part of reality, and the fact that we cannot see energy flowing through space detracts nothing from our understanding that the flow is real.

Thus we begin firmly to grasp in comprehension the truth that our minds oftentimes can see what our eyes cannot. And so we progress even to the point of understanding that what the eye sees may be less real than that which it fails to see. The "real" is understood to be unreality, and the invisible at times to be the true reality.

One step more, and mind sees that total reality consists far more of energy as electromagnetism and gravity than of

---

[2]By 1963, the number of original published items relating to Fuller's work had grown to over 300 per annum; by 1968, to 2100 per annum.

[3]Fuller's patents have included those of such primary significance as to have stimulated widespread demand for licenses by manufacturers and governments seeking to reap benefit from their use.

energy as substance—as "substance" was thought of before. Astronomically more, we have learned to say in our minds, hard as it still may be to grasp such an elusive concept.[4]

The mind of genius, accepting such a concept more readily, instinctively probes deeper into the unseen world of force. Richard Buckminster Fuller in sincerest modesty is insistent upon his belief that his discoveries have always come to him "intuitively." Certain it is that in reaching his most fundamental breakthrough points he has hurdled swiftly past many walls of prior scientific thought. The primary *modus operandi* of his mind causes him to see the whole of anything before he begins to analyze its parts. This is strikingly illustrated by his new geometry which, in full revelation of his personal dynamism, he has aptly entitled, Energetic and Synergetic Geometry. It is a geometry which has been found helpful to advanced thinkers in diverse fields, particularly so in that of nuclear physics.

Now comes the problem of how best to explain Fuller's discoveries when we understand that the most fundamental of them probe so deeply into the unseen dynamics of force and precession. The biographers and journalists as a rule have sought to explain Fuller's works against a backdrop of profuse illustration. The inventor himself is an exponent of the use of models and pictures and uses these with telling effect in teaching his university students. This is all very well when the presentation is given life and meaning by Professor Fuller's unique teaching in which a strong tide of ideas rapidly submerges first of all the pictures, then the language of ordinary speech, and finally even the shorthand of the teacher's own special language invented to supply a deficiency in dictionary terms. Fuller has needed, used and successfully communicated ideas with self-contrived semantics which often convey his expanding meanings by a process

---

[4] "In Einstein's $E = Mc^2$, M is less than 1% of universe totality." Note to the text by R. B. F.

which the student himself may not be able to analyze. He knows only that he understands, not how.

The present effort to furnish a comprehensive explanation of the fundamental nature of Fuller's inventions and discoveries is partly an experiment. Can words convey the scope of inventive breakthrough with deeper insight than pictures? Perhaps even than pictures explained? An example which quickly comes to mind is the pictorial representation of the Fuller geodesic dome. The mind of the viewer, more often than not, is distracted by the picture so that he is not piqued into asking, "Why geodesic, what does that mean?" The more usual questions are, "How big is it?," and "What is it made of?" Big enough to cover a football field or even a city. And a geodesic dome can be made of just about anything—steel, aluminum, plastics, wood, even paper. It has in fact been built of all these materials. But a more truly revealing answer, once explained, is that a geodesic dome really is made of "geometry." It is in a sense a mathematical discovery which enables the builder to use with far greater effectiveness the inherent tensile strength of whatever material he may employ, so that "less material makes more dome." So the core of understanding must be created by subjoined explanation of how this comes to pass.

Dante portrayed the dynamic "flowing" mathematics of his poetic vision of God with words unaided, thinking of himself "as the geometer, intent to scan the measure of the circle."[5] It seems certain that the poet could not have succeeded so well had graphic representation been allowed to intrude. The reader, upon viewing an illustration, at first sees in it whatever his own education and experience permits him to find there. What he sees may well set him off the trail of the knowledge he pursues. Especially so when a geodesic dome cannot possibly self-explain its unseen mathematical virtues to the uninitiated. Bucky Fuller on occasion used to

---

[5]The Divine Comedy, Paradiso, Canto xxxiii.

disclose to us, by transcontinental or transoceanic telephone, the concept of some new idea, using only the illustrations his words made visible to the mind, unhampered by visual concreteness.

With that much encouragement by Fuller's own example, let us now embark upon our adventure into the largely invisible but very real world of Buckminster Fuller as revealed through his discoveries and inventions.

Chapter 2

SPHERICAL INTEGRITY FOR A FLAT MAP OF THE ROUND WORLD

"I think I have found something pretty exciting." Buckminster Fuller was warming up to the prospect of explaining a new concept to his patent lawyer. From the restrained eagerness in the soft voice and the sparkle in the inventor's eye, you could tell that it was going to be well worth the listening. When Bucky opened a conversation that way, you knew you had to listen hard. Good chance that your powers of concentration and imagining were going to be stressed to their tensile limits. But if you could hold fast to the tumbling torrent of thought, you were certain to be rewarded with some deep insight that would indeed be "pretty exciting," as Bucky had promised.

More often than not, such a session would see a mealtime or bedtime fly past unheeded. As the inventor's story unfolded, and some new world of scientific and philosophic revelation was breaking through the mists of imperfect understanding, you almost could become a little giddy. Ideas can achieve a richness that possesses an inebriating quality, and the fresh thrusts of Bucky's unfettered imagination made a heady potion.

Celestial bodies responding to immutable laws of gravity and motion whirl in stately procession inexorably through time. Their movements within the symmetry of orbital flight are forever curving, oblivious to man's unreal world of arbitrary straight lines and "immovable" objects. He, plodding with ant-like persistence along the enticing thin, straight lines of Euclidean thought, responds to a system of statics which in turn almost is oblivious to the whirling universe which his eyes cannot see. His habitual thought process, inwardly directed, so blurs the focus of his imaginative power as only to increase his difficulty in perceiving the more comprehensive truths of the world in which he lives and has his being.

How strange it now seems that in olden times men conceived that the world was flat. Yet such a view is only one manifestation of man's seeming insistence that the whole of mathematics, science and architecture must be generated from beginning concepts of straight lines and flat planes. Ultimately, through development of these concepts with the use of more straight lines as radial generators, his ancient geometry brings him to the cylinder and the sphere, but it has been a long way round red robin's barn. When beginning Euclid, he was taught that, "A straight line is the shortest distance between two points." Later on, if ever he was called upon to work out an ordinary problem of "the sailings" in navigation, he found to his chagrin that in order to sail the shortest distance between two points, he must pursue a "great circle" course which on his chart isn't a straight line but a curved one!

And now, brought into crisp focus by a mind swept clear of the limitations of old geometry, the idea which the inventor thought "pretty exciting" began to unfold. "The problem of the navigator is how to sail (or fly) the shortest course, which on a conventional chart will be a curved line." Bucky paused, studying his listener's face for sign of full attention, then continued. "I simply design an unconventional chart which is so constructed that all future navigators can find their courses as straight lines. This means that I will need a new kind of map projection in which all great circles of a sphere will be seen as straight lines." It will be noticed that in Fuller's eyes the first step would be to break away altogether from existing concepts so that he could start afresh in hope of reaching a more comprehensive solution. No thought of simply trying to improve on the older systems of map projection. Begin again from the very beginning. Let no old thought intrude, however hallowed by time.

Strange as it may now seem for pre-Copernicus man to have imagined that the world was flat, it can be thought even stranger that once having discovered that his flatish notion was foolish and unreal, he still persisted in holding tenaciously to the equally foolish notion that the parallels of latitude must appear as straight lines on a chart poorly suited to the navigator's needs in sailing a course about his new round world! Knowing it was round was comforting, as he would not sail off the edge of it. But he still had to contend with the awkwardness of a chart which in a most arbitrary fashion retained so peculiar a use of the seemingly indispensable straight line. So peculiar, in fact, as to represent what is *not* the shortest distance between two points, and which has no validity as a scale of distance. Only along the Equator or by following a great circle meridian could the sailor find true distance, or plot the shortest course as a straight line. These were special cases not often to be encountered in the realm of practical navigation. What was needed, reasoned Fuller, was a solution that somehow could bring greater spherical integrity to a flat map of the round world.

"As the Earth is a spherical body, so the only true cartographic representation of its surface must be spherical," said Fuller, adding, "All flat surface maps are compromises with truth." Mercator's projection, we know, is true to scale only along the Equator, so that Alaska, Greenland and all far northern lands are stretched beyond any semblance of reality. Azimuthal projection is limited to conversion of the meridians at one pole at a time. Other systems of projection known before Fuller's cartography came into being in 1943-44, could be made to give uniform scale along parallels, or to yield other fragments of spherical integrity. Any comprehensive verity in a world map was still lacking, and it remained for

21

Fuller to point the way to flat-mapping the world with a new kind of world-around integrity of scale.

Fuller's fresh approach to this age-old problem of the map makers was to resolve the Earth's surface into sections which are entirely bounded by projections of great circles. To begin with, this could be made to give the complete truth, and nothing but the truth, along the boundary of every section of the map. The navigator would need only to measure the distance along these great circle boundaries to know his answer in true nautical miles. It was like Equator or meridian sailings multiplied to cover the earth in a comprehensive network of true-distance lines.

Next, while maintaining all these "truth boundaries," the projection of land and water features from the spherical to the flat surfaces according to the inventor's cartography, brought the "subsidence" distortion, that is the distortion enforced by translation from sphere to plane, to an irreducible minimum. This might be explained by thinking of an orange peel section squeezed flat without stretching or breaking its edges as compared with another orange peel section which is perhaps more tender and splays out at the edge when pushed flat. The first orange peel, flattened, continues to portray true edge measurements of its section; the second has lost all capacity to give any true measurements except that at its unbroken center, there is a single point remaining as it was in the orange. But only a point, not a line. Nothing that could be measured to show true scale or distance. What Fuller did, then, was to discover how to use a grid of intersecting great circles for geometric translation of a sphere into a plane. These were his great circles of truth, a concept neatly fitting the intuitive dynamics of the man, circles being inherently representative of energy and motion as opposed to statics.

Logic, progressing with measured steps of unerring dignity in a straight line from premise to conclusion, is deceptive. Turtle-like, it moves slowly and commendably to a short-sighted goal. An imagination such as Fuller's whirls without restraint, encompassing whole new galaxies of thought. One can almost literally see Fuller's whirling pattern of thought within the geometrically wound ball of yarn wrapped into its overall maze of great circles. Unwrapped, they become a map of greater truth than any before.

Here, then, we perceive the meaning and worth of Fuller's habitual exercise of comprehensive thought. There is first the whole, consisting of a network of intersecting great circles, the open mesh of the net filled again with great circle gridding, and only after that the resolution, or taking apart, into the pieces which are to be assembled, puzzle-wise, into a map. At first the whole; comprehensiveness. The result of the comprehensive thought procedure in this instance brought into being a world map[1], which gives a truer overall picture of areas, boundaries, directions and distances than had been provided before by any known system of map projection.

---

[1]United States patent No. 2,393,676, granted January 29, 1946.

Chapter 3

ENERGETIC AND SYNERGETIC GEOMETRY

AT first the whole; comprehensiveness. In college at Harvard, Fuller's intuitive mind soon forced him to reexamine the validity of the Euclidean-imagined straight line, and of a geometry built upon static concepts. Instinctively he felt the need to find a real, not an imaginary, starting point. Imagination is all well and good, but let it spring from a real base, not one that imagination itself, uninformed, has contrived. That base, to Fuller's mind, must be broad, and, to be truly comprehensive, should consist of nothing less than the "totality of human experience." A large order, but the faculty for comprehensive thinking could settle for nothing less. The truth impulse must be uncompromising, and "uncompromising" in present context is merely a synonym for "comprehensive." In any case, Fuller's comprehensive mind refused compromise with Euclid's imaginary, static-world straight line. Out of this staunch refusal was born a new-world geometry, aptly termed "Energetic and Synergetic Geometry." It began, not with an imaginary straight line, but with a comprehensive sweeping view of the universe around us, moving, dynamic, orbiting, complete.

Students in universities throughout eastern and western worlds were introduced to a new world of mathematical concept when the man they would grow to think of with affection simply as "Bucky" commanded their minds to fresh vigor of creative effort. Beginning his explanation of the new geometry, he would say, holding before his class a simple model consisting of three triangles hinged together in a chain,

"One equilateral triangle . . .

"Hinged to two others . . .

"Can be folded into a three-sided 'tent' whose base *is a fourth triangle.*"

Having suited action to the words, he tilts the tent backwards to show the base triangle.

"Now," Bucky continues with mounting excitement, "The *inadvertent* appearance of this *fourth* triangle is a demonstration of 'synergy,' which is the behavior of a system unpredicted by its parts:

$$"1 + 2 = 4"$$

Then, to drive home to his students the essential need for them to comprehend the totality of a problem, he would say,

"A triangle drawn on the Earth's surface is actually a spherical triangle bounded by great circle arcs." (Think of the Equator; it is a "great" circle as distinguished from, say, the fortieth parallel of latitude which is a "lesser" circle; all great circles of the earth, be they the Equator, the meridians, or otherwise, would be equal in measurement to the nominal 25,000 miles of earth's circumference.)[1]

"If the triangle is drawn large enough," Fuller continues, "its edges will reach an 'equator' which will divide the surface of the earth into two triangles enclosed by common edges." And right here Fuller comes to the point of his proof of the need to comprehend the totality of a problem:

"Now, because every spherical surface has two aspects—

---

[1] "A triangle as an area bounded by a closed line of three edges and three angles drawn upon the Earth sphere must divide the total surface of the sphere into two areas, one on either side of the closed line both of which being bounded by three edges and three angles must be triangles—one a very large one, the other a very small one." Note to the text by R. B. F.

convex if viewed from outside, concave if from within—*each of these triangles is, in itself, two triangles.*"

And then, eyes sparkling, Fuller would say, "Thus one triangle becomes four *when the total complex is understood.*" Fuller's excitement was contagious as the students' minds were tethered to his in search for broader understanding of the total complex. Now, if we ourselves can join minds with Fuller's as he explains the rudiments of energetic and synergetic geometry, we may succeed in laying aside some of our Euclidean certainties and enjoy the exhilaration of stretching those brain cells of ours to gain comprehension of totality.

It was not that Fuller wanted to find fault with Euclid. After all, that was a pre-Copernicus geometry and in its inception could not avail of a round-world concept. An imagined flat world naturally would incubate an imaginary flat plane, Euclid's built-up second dimension. It was simply that Fuller was somehow intuitively compelled to clear his mind of the mathematical precepts which had stood for so long in their deceptive simplicity that they had become almost beyond strength of challenge.

And so, with the whole of human knowledge and experience as his point of departure, Fuller was able to find a comprehensive geometry capable of bringing into congruence form, mass, external space, the energies of heat, electrostatics, electrodynamics, electric waves and, finally, "the atomic complexities demonstrated by the family of chemical elements." Once freed from the unreal world of a static Euclid, the innate dynamics of Fuller's mind not only brought forth this revelation of an exquisite congruence of form, mass and energy experience, but also led to the discovery of the inventor's "closest packing" theory. A leading nuclear physicist, speaking of Fuller's concept of closest packing, has acknowledged this theory to be "an indispensable aid to understanding the significance of advanced studies" in his field.[2]

------

[2]See, A Periodic Table for Fundamental Particles, John J. Grebe, New York Academy of Sciences, Volume 76, Article 1.

The new geometry begins quite simply and directly with an investigation of requirements for a minimum system within the universe. A ball on a string, the end of the string being held at a fixed point, is free to spin at the limit of its tether in a myriad of circular arcs. The fixed point at the end of the string furnishes what is functionally described as a single vector of restraint. The locus of the path of movement of the ball as tethered by this single vector of restraint defines a sphere—a three-dimensional system. With two vectors of restraint as provided where the ball is held by two strings fixed to anchorages at opposite sides of the ball (a pendulum plus its mirror image), a plane is defined—a two-dimensional system. Three vectors of restraint (three strings and three anchorages), and a line is scribed—a one-dimensional system. Four vectors, and a point is fixed with no displacement possible in any direction. Notice how completely Euclid has been turned upside down, Euclid beginning with the "straight" line and eventually building up to a solid, Fuller with the sphere which is the comprehensive whole that represents the totality of experience—the totality which is to be analyzed and comprehended.

Continuing beyond these initial thought structures, Fuller's geometry of energy and synergy advances to concepts of "turbining" within the position otherwise fixed by the four vectors of restraint, and to the basic revelation that the four vectors define the tetrahedron, a polyhedron having four equal equilateral faces. This remarkable figure, the tetrahedron, is the first identifiable "system" as a primary or minimum division of Universe.

Extension of the edges of the tetrahedron through any one vertex creates a kind of triangular hour-glass which forms what a complete understanding will describe as "positive" and "negative" tetrahedrons (a tetrahedron and its mirror image). This is another example of the two-ness of a system. The one noticed before was the two-ness of a spherical triangle which is both convex and concave.

28

The Universe must be the starting point for any study of synergetic phenomena. "Universe" is defined as the sum total of all man's sensed and communicated experience. The within-ness and without-ness of a spherical (concave-convex) surface suggests the inherent two-ness of the Universe.

Proceeding beyond the discovery of the first identifiable system, the tetrahedron, Fuller's exposition demonstrates that the mathematical process of "squaring" is equivalent to "triangling" (edge times edge equals area), while "cubing" is equivalent to "tetrahedroning" (edge times edge times edge equals volume). A little thought about these two mathematical equivalents will quickly make apparent the intellectual block-busting potential of such revolutionary concepts to the mathematician and scientist.

Such is the enticing introduction to the geometry of energy and synergy; the new-school geometry of Universe. In its further development, this geometry reaches what has come to be known as geodesic structuring, according to which the largest free-span structures in the world have been erected. And it has found surprising points of congruence in the field of medicine, where such geodesic structuring has been identified by molecular biologists with the structure of the protein shell that surrounds every known virus. Logically, it can be imagined that a truly comprehensive system would in certainty create bridges across all of the chasms in man's compartmented world. A comprehensive system should be valid in mechanics, electronics, chemistry, biology, medicine, astronomy . . .

Fuller's method of comprehensive thought is to go behind the "known" theory and begin once more at the experimentally informed beginning, being careful to avoid distraction by scientific dogma, mind alert to examine fresh approaches and to formulate new interpretations of what men understood, or thought they understood, before. The strongest and most unique characteristic of Fuller's mind is that it allows no thought that springs solely from any one point. "Intuitively," as Fuller uses the term in self-analysis, the cocooning fabric of thought is spun between a complex of points as it inventories and reconsiders the broadest possible range of relevant experience in quest of universal truth, the truth of the whole. The purity and one-ness of the patterns evolved by such a method is itself a demonstration of the phenomenon of synergy, according to which the whole is equal to more than the sum of its recognized parts.

Chapter 4

TENSILE INTEGRITY IN ARCHITECTURE

NOWHERE is Fuller's comprehensive approach more vividly portrayed for all to see and comprehend than in the field of architecture. In this instance, what exactly, is meant when we say, "comprehensive"? Well, to begin with, Fuller does not at first think abstractly of architecture by itself. That would be yielding to a restraint imposed by the chains of old thought which generated the notion that architecture is something which can be placed off in a compartment by itself. Rather he thinks of man and his environment as he ponders the broad range of man's experience in housing himself against the elements.[1] This is translated into everyday language as (a) selection and use of materials, (b) ascertainment of the manner in which the selected materials can be used to greatest economic advantage, (c) study of the feasibility of prefabricating components of the ultimate structure (or, as with some of Full-

---

[1]"By 'environment,' I refer to everything that isn't me. Since experimental science has found no continuums, no solids, no straight lines, no infinity, no simultaneity, no permanence, but only constantly transforming dynamic event patterns, the concept of 'thingness' is invalid. There are only events, no things. Only verbs, no nouns. Therefore, all of the universe that isn't me consists of events. Those events range from the very large and infrequent to the very small and frequent. The environment is a complex of such small to large ranging events which impinge upon me from outside me and from inside me. I can intercept and deflect angularly all such detected events and shunt them into preferred holding patterns to be valved purposefully into my thus regenerating organism in preferred and complementary rather than destructive increments and time coordinations." Note to the text by R. B. F.

31

er's architecture, prefabricating the entire structure), (d) analysis of the logistics of transporting the materials, components or finished structure to the erecting site. This is not the end of the list, nor is there necessarily any such formal outline in Fuller's mind, his being the more comprehensive unstyled contemplation of the whole of man's environment in its relation to the "architectural" problem at hand. It is just that his intellect, free from inhibition, is touching and sorting multiple facets of man's "sensed and translated experience" as it permits itself to reach, intuitively, new crystallization of experience into a more perfect unity. The crystal of thought so formed will be fresh and sparkling in its purity of conception within a frame of reference that is at once mathematical, dynamic, and conscious of Universe as a whole. That crystal in the present instance becomes the "geodesic" dome; a structure capable of enclosing most space per ounce of material used, and which utilizes synergetically the ultimate quantum of available tensile strength properties of that material.

Through milleniums of history, man, with endless persistence and inexhaustible patience, has piled stone on stone, log on log, beam on column. In the process, he selected materials that would best resist crushing, for his plan was to carry loads in compression. As an exception to the rule stood the tepees and other tent forms of the nomadic tribes of Indians and Arabs. Tents, however, were not translatable to the needs of society generally, and the lesson that they might have taught in the use of tensile strength of lighter weight materials never reached beyond field camps for the military and the circus tent. The Iron Age brought the steel girder, an assembly of parts some of which were placed in tension, but the majority of which still relied on the ancient scheme of using the compressive, or columnar, strength of the girder elements. Then there was the suspension bridge whose cables utilized the tensile properties of the steel wire from which the cables were spun. But in houses and buildings, when tensioned elements were used at all, these were only incidental to the great scheme of a piled-up structure, standing as a ponderous reminder of the pyramids of Egypt. Compression was still King of the forces. This, notwithstanding the fact that the technologies of metallurgy, glass fibre making, and of chemistry in plastics, had developed significant improvement in the tensile properties of materials, whereas comparatively little could be done to increase strength in compression. Fuller observed, "If we have better metallurgical alloys, we can make longer and longer tension members with less and less section—apparently ad infinitum, but *not* longer and thinner compression columns, ad infinitum."

Such was the setting of the stage when the scene of building history shifted, and there stood Fuller's "geodesic" dome, made of mind and geometry. It was an extremely lightweight, spidery structure whose parts interacted with one another in a most remarkable tensile network. Previously, Fuller had invented a round house supported from a central mast. This, too, had been designed with the objective of making better use of the tensile strength of building materials. Concerning this unusual form of house, Fuller was asked, "Why do you build a house that is round?" His quick response was, "Why do you build one that is square?" Then, answering his own question, "Originally, a log house came out square because the logs were straight, making the sides of the house straight. An Eskimo did not experience this limitation, and perhaps intuitively since nature made men's skulls spheroidal rather than cubical, he made his igloo in the form of a dome uniquely suited to his needs, being easy to heat efficiently, and providing the greatest amount of living volume per block of ice used in its construction. So now," Fuller explained patiently, "we have building materials which are admirably suited to the erection of structures without any limitation as to their form. This affords us the opportunity of building more efficiently and to greater functional advantage."

33

Above all, Fuller had been seeking a way of using man's material building resources to best possible advantage. The greatest unused potential of the properties of available materials lay in their tensile strengths. To his mind, comprehending at first only the totality of the problem, and unfettered to any preconceived notions of form or structuring, the assignment was exciting in the freedom of choice he afforded himself. No idea of doing the unconventional, but just the innate urge to find the "minimum system for enclosing space," regardless of whether or not it be conventional. He was not going to be conventional for the sake of conforming to what was accepted, but neither was he concerned with any need to depart from the norm. Perhaps, as with atonal music, he was only being "a-conventional." He simply had to find the one best answer, the ultimate solution.

This was a matter which concerned conservation of the world's material resources, and was not to be taken lightly. It was an inseparable part of his philosophy, which he formulated in these carefully chosen words: "The possibility of the good life for any man depends upon the possibility of realizing it for all men. And this is a function of society's ability to turn the energies of the universe to human advantage." In the new architecture of geodesics, human advantage was to be sought through maximum utilization of tensile force, or, as he was wont to express it, through maximum "tensile integrity" in architecture. In his classroom shorthand, "Tensegrity."

Buckminster Fuller's geodesic dome patent,[2] entitled simply, "Building Construction," is a remarkable document as patents go. To begin with, the fundamental nature of the inventive concept had at once created a new language of its own. As with the radio and the telephone, the geodesic dome was a pioneer, and a new dictionary was needed to name it and to designate its new parts. The patent includes a sec-

---

[2]United States patent No. 2,682,235, granted June 29, 1954.

tion entitled, "Definition of Terms," these being terms which have come to be used in the new art of geodesic construction with special connotation—terms such as "icosacap," "three-way great circle grid," "modularly divided," and "frequency."

The structure is described as being spherical, or having the form of a portion of a sphere; or, it can be polygonal, a "faceted" sphere. The individual structural elements are so arranged as to be aligned with great circles of a sphere. Seven years earlier, Fuller had discovered how, in the field of cartography, surprising advantages accrued through the use of "great circles." So here we have another indication of the comprehensive nature of Fuller's inventorship, for it finds a least common denominator for inventions in map-making and architecture, just as his discoveries in the field of mathematics found congruence in nuclear physics and molecular biology. Fuller has suggested the possibility that the ultimate in comprehensive discovery could some day reduce "inventing" to a purely mathematical process. Certain it is that the more man comprehends, the greater is the range of new ideas that appear to him to be obvious, whereas in the patenting of inventions, the law says that only the unobvious is patentable.

To pursue Fuller's suggestion concerning the application of mathematics to inventing by considering what may be a case in point, we might well investigate what influence Fuller's comprehensive discovery of the new geometry could have had in leading to his invention of the geodesic dome. We have noticed that early in his presentation of energetic/synergetic geometry, Fuller stressed the point that a triangle drawn on the Earth's surface is actually a spherical triangle bounded by great circle arcs. And, a moment ago, we learned that in describing the geodesic dome, the inventor explained that its structural elements are aligned with great circles of a sphere. Hence we see that the "great circles" of the geometry reappeared in the structuring of the geodesic dome. If we were to continue our investigation into a deeper stratum of

35

analysis, we would discover another common base between the geometry and geodesics, for it turns out that in the geodesic dome, Fuller has called upon that "first identifiable system of Universe," the tetrahedron, and its stabilizing vector system.

Thinking first only of the great circles as a least common denominator of geometry and dome, we may ask, "How would Fuller arrange these circles?" The patent document states with definitive geometry that the circles are to lie in planes which contain the vertexes of a polyhedron. So much for definition with the range of acceptable Patent Office semantics. The fact is that Fuller did not "arrange" the circles in the sense that one would arrange beams in a conventional building. He permitted nature, or nature's geometry, to do it. Besides that most remarkable tetrahedron with its stabilizing vector system, there was also the icosahedron complex which was capable of bringing that vector system into play for a spherical breakdown useful in dome architecture.

By this time it must be reasonably clear that the pattern of inventive thought which created the geodesic dome was strongly influenced by the compatible inventive pattern which brought energetic/synergetic geometry into being. We need not decide the validity of Fuller's thought that the ultimate in comprehensive discovery could one day reduce all inventing to a mathematical process. Perhaps that could happen only in the case of "genius" inventing, having a depth of perceptive analysis such as Fuller's.

Fuller's genius flourished in the climate of his ability to strike from mental consciousness every shred of prior analysis, so as in effect to create a vacuum into which might flow the perceptiveness of new natural thought. The observed phenomena of nature can then create greater purity and depth of perception—an intuitive awareness akin to what Fuller has described as "the extraordinary moments of purely poetical lucidities of man." It must almost certainly have been just such an extraordinary moment which brought to

Fuller's mind the concept of how the geometry that was "Nature's own," would arrange the great circles to best advantage in architecture. The icosahedron, expressing that geometry, exploded onto the surface of a sphere, did the job that the patent described in definitive terms as "great circles which contain the vertexes of a polyhedron."

The icosahedron is a figure having twenty equal, equilateral faces. Uniquely, the icosahedron has an inversion, or *alter ego,* in the dodecahedron, a figure which has twelve equal, equilateral faces. Whichever is considered as the starting point in the geometry of solids, the resulting pattern of great circles comes out the same. This is a third example of the two-ness of the universe as observed by Fuller in the cases of the convex-concave spherical triangle and of the tetrahedral "hour-glass."

It is quite essential that we notice these mathematical probes in order to comprehend the scope of Fuller's thought pattern. We then can perceive in some measure the dynamism of a mind that moves in ever accelerating curve toward infinitude of understanding in which "the whole of man's sensed and translated experience" finds congruence—in which mathematics, physics, chemistry, and biology will one day be seen only as parts of a greater whole which, responding to unifying force, reveals an exquisite underlying pattern of the motion that is life itself. Advancing far through the distances to that day of great understanding, Fuller has already identified a system which links together geometry, cartography, virus structuring and geodesic architecture.

The architect's great circles, defined by intersections with a sphere of planes passing through the vertexes of those peculiar polyhedrons, "icosa" and "dodeca," create a sophisticated relationship. Used as the patterning of geodesic domes, and superimposing what geodesic designers call "three-way gridding," the circles and grids produce a uniformity in overall pattern that is at once apparent even to an unpracticed eye. The visual manifestations of the pattern are many and surprisingly varied. In one there is a total complex of equilateral triangles. In another, diamonds. In a third, hexagons, but revealing a number of pentagons as well which, upon careful examination, are found to occur at each of the twelve vertexes of the originating icosahedron. This demonstrates that the integrity of the icosa has been preserved.

What is the true worth of these distinctive patterns in terms of structural advantages, it is logical to ask. Answer: a building erected according to such a pattern is exceptionally strong and possesses optimum stability, being inherently capable of distributing stresses from here to there or, more accurately, from any point to the structure as a whole. When a force is applied so that its loading is concentrated at a single point, the tendency to deform the structure at that point will be resisted by the total complex of the framework —much as a rubber ball will absorb the impact of its bounce.

A further perspective is gained by comparing geodesic construction with that of the familiar form of dome in which supporting arches converge to intersect one another at the apex. Imagining the apex to be one of the poles of a world globe, the sides of the arches will appear as the meridians of longitude. Through the arches, forces or loading applied to this form of dome are transmitted to a single point of congruence at the apex, or "pole," where they are concentrated, rather than distributed. This, then, is "polarized" structuring. Geodesics, the antithesis of this, is non-polarized and force-distributing.

To some eyes, the strangeness of geodesic structuring sets it rather apart from practical building norms, taking as the norm the more conventional forms of past and present. This means of course the familiar vertically-walled building and its variations. Of these, Fuller states, "They are buildings which want to fall down, and so must be braced and gusseted against doing so." And adds, "Whereas geodesic domes just naturally want to stand up." It is a tribute to the soundness of geodesic design and engineering that unconventionality of form and construction has not prevented its use and acclaim throughout the world for many purposes less well served before. Licensed to some eighty manufacturers, the geodesic dome has been constructed of steel, aluminum, magnesium, wood, plastics—even of paperboard. Light, compact as capsuled for shipment, the domes have been airlifted to building sites otherwise inaccessible, as at polar bases and even in the mountain fastnesses of the Himalayas. Size of geodesic buildings seems virtually without any limitation. They have been built in sizes big enough to cover a football field, and designs have been engineered for structures that can provide weatherbreaks for entire cities. Even an abbreviated list of geodesic projects completed would be less than representative without mention of dome houses for earthquake relief, weatherbreaks for electronic defense warning systems, domes for trade fairs around the world, United States Marine Corps shelters and the United States Pavilion at the World's Fair at Montreal, Canada. It seems a portent for the future that there is a manufacturer of educational geodesic building sets from which today's children will be able to learn about geodesic geometry by putting together icosa-form structures.

Architectural students throughout the United States now know the language of geodesics, as do others in Africa, India and Japan. Knowing this, all should want to understand something about this fundamentally new concept in architecture. More importantly, it should be understood for what it truly is, a comprehensive answer to the question: How can the world utilize to its greatest commonweal the prodigious strength of materials in tension? What geodesics comes down to is:

The invention of a structure that uses tension to higher advantage. A structure of greater tensile integrity. In a new word, "Tensegrity."

THE United States patent on geodesic construction was granted in 1954. By the end of 1955, the dynamic concepts of geodesics and tensegrity were beginning to stir the minds of engineers and architects. In that brief moment of history, eight corporations had sought and obtained licenses under the patent and were busy manufacturing geodesic structures in wood, steel, aluminum and magnesium. The United States Marine Corps had discovered that geodesics opened the way to a whole new logistics for swift movement of troops and supplies, and was ordering production of geodesic shelters which could be air-lifted to advance bases. These were put together as a framework of magnesium struts supporting skins of tensioned nylon plastic in uncompromising acceptance of the fundamentals of tensile integrity.

But the questing mind of Buckminster Fuller at this moment of acceptance did not pause in contemplation of his personally engineered triumph for tensile architecture, for it was busy racing toward the forever of the future. Unable to accept magnesium and nylon as necessarily being the ultimate in rebellion against man's self-imposed burden of stone and steel, the eye of his mind plummeted on in its search for a surpassing perfection. What even greater use might be made of the energy of the universe for benefit of man? What material could be lighter than the lightest metal skinned with a froth of nylon? Cardboard? "Ridiculous," you say? To Fuller, no answer was to be rejected by hitching it to the ball and chain of castigation. No, cardboard might do the job. Paper on edge, as a column would support nothing heavier than a fly. But it does have tearing strength—tensile strength.

Thus was born another invention concerned with the fundamental philosophy of turning the energy of the universe to greatest human advantage. And so, almost before the signatures of Fuller's eight pioneering manufacturers

40

were dry on their geodesic licenses, there came into being at the advent of the new year 1955, an application to patent the "paper" building. This was a structure which, in correct appraisal, could only be described as being made of cellulose and the geometry of geodesics plus a still newer increment of tensile integrity. Four years later, the patent granted on that application gave official recognition to the newer increment by the allowance of claims which define tensile stressing of paperboard components of a geodesic dome. Because the geodesic dome itself is a tension structure possessing what is known as tensile integrity, the use in that structure of a component which has been stressed in tension, produces an exquisite compounding of tensile force patterns. In Fuller's starkly revealing semantics, this is explained as a tensile integrity of both structured component and structured dome.

To form an idea of the nature of this force complex, the first step will be to visualize how the individual structured component is made and stressed. In the beginning, there is only a simple rectangular piece of paperboard. It is scored to create two fold lines lengthwise of the rectangle, and two crosswise, then bent first round the lengthwise folds into a tube having three flat walls—a tube of triangular section. The tube is then bent around its crosswise folds into a triangular picture frame. Gores cut at the crosswise folds allow the frame to take its intended shape without rupturing. At this point there has been formed a triangular frame each of whose three sides is a three-faced tube, that is, triangular in cross section.

Now appears the new increment of tensioning. Its dynamics will not be visible, but can be explained:

When the tube is being folded into a triangular frame, the material of the tube is "crowded" at the corners of the frame. This is a function of the special design of the gores and flaps adjacent the crosswise folds. The intentional crowding of the material at the corners of the frame has the result of applying tension to the outside of the frame. It is this tension which affords tensile integrity of the structured component of the dome in which it will become a part of the inherent geodesic stress pattern.

Now as the number of such tensile components is multiplied, while adhering to integrity of the geometry of geodesics as one component may vary undiscernably from another according to what is known as the frequency of the particular dome design selected, there will have been created all of the basic structural elements needed to construct a building that will inherently provide what Fuller encapsulates in his phrase, "tensile integrity of both structured component and structured dome."

By coating the paperboard with a plastic before the rectangular pieces are tension-folded, the tensile aspect of the building is further increased by reason of the utilization of the tensile strength of a plastic film. The result is a building which in a very real sense derives its strength from "paper and paint," plus that priceless new ingredient, tensile integrity compounded.

When the family of interrelated tensioned triangles is brought together in its geodesic geometry of a completed dome, two events occur, one that can be seen, another that cannot. The first is the visible mating of the several members of the family into the characteristic beauty of geodesic pattern. The second is the invisible mating of tensile integrities, and it is the event of greater significance to man in his strivings to afford himself more of the blessings of nature.

At almost the same moment that Fuller was readying his disclosure of this invention for presentation to the Patent Office, the dome of paper and geometry was being shown in Milan, where, at the Triennale Exhibition, it won for the United States the grand prize in architecture.

The patent was granted.[3]

---

[3]U.S. patent, No. 2,881,717, granted April 14, 1959.

AS Fuller's new art of geodesics brought a forward gain for all men through optimum use of tensile force to conserve material, so also did it reduce man's labor in transport and building, for none of the material that was saved needed to be handled. But there was still more to it than that. In the beauty of its simplicity, the geodesic structure had fewer parts, and could be built within a tiny fraction of the time needed for erection of more conventional structures. Hence it could sooner be made ready for occupancy and use. Here was another dividend of the comprehensive approach:

Time, the fourth dimension of geodesics. The equation becomes

$$\text{Tensile integrity} = \text{conservation of material resources} + \text{conservation of time.}$$

The sum of Fuller's success in geodesics thus can be expressed as a four-dimensional "ability of society to turn the energies of the universe to human advantage."

In 1956, the United States Information Agency decided that it would like to have a pavilion at the international trade fair in Kabul, Afghanistan. Kabul was not accessible by railroad or highway. The problem was how to transport and erect a big enough building of any kind in such an inaccessible spot. Air transport could be the only solution, but sending a building by air would be a large order!

Sixty days later and the building wished for was there in faraway Kabul, erected and ready for use as the United States pavilion, an 8,000 square foot geodesic dome of 117 feet clearspan diameter. Within that sixty days, the pavilion had been conceived, its spherical geometry calculated, its drawings made, its components manufactured, assembled, tested, disassembled and packaged for shipment, loaded into a single DC-4 cargo plane, flown to a building site halfway round the world, and erected. The erection time was twenty-four hours.

A photograph of the Kabul dome appears in the United States patent that was granted to cover this further advance in the geodesic art.[4] Fuller had discovered that if he combined a geodesic frame with a geodesically patterned plastic skin, these two structural complexes would interact one with the other in a very special way. The secret was to make the two structures, frame and skin, "conform in structure, pattern or behavior to a mutual three way great circle synergy." He described the effect in these words:

> [It] gives a new and synergetic stress distribution—synergetic in the sense that the behavior of the skin under stress is unpredicted by its several parts, and there is imparted to the structure a strength beyond that which would be calculated using accepted values of strengths of materials and usual methods of stress analysis and computation.

The skin could be made of either flexible or rigid materials so that in one sense it could be an outwardly framed tent, or in another a domed building, of compound geodesic stress characteristics.

If we wish to comprehend more firmly the course of the inventor's stream of thought, and appreciate its motion, we will notice the vitality of his recurrent emphasis on dynamics. Never just materials in static concept, but forces in a more abstract sense. It seems almost to be an inversion of the ordinary engineering that thinks of forces as being applied to materials. With Fuller, it is the force that is first in contemplation, while the material is secondary. Too, we will notice a pervasive understanding of the reality of synergy as opposed to the unreality of ordinary mathematics. As with the "inadvertent appearance of a fourth triangle" in the example given (*supra*, page 26) which made "1 + 2 = 4," we now have

---

[4]No. 2,914,074, granted November 24, 1959.

the synergetic effect of two great circle structures interacting one with the other. Additionally, we will notice that in all his inventions, the map, the geodesic structures, and in others to be discussed, Fuller's thoughts never lose touch with the mathematics of his own energetic and synergetic geometry, nor with a deep philosophical awareness of the existence of an exquisite underlying pattern in the entire universe of man's experience.

It can scarcely be doubted that it is these several ingredients of Fuller's comprehensive outlook which bring to his inventions that fundamental character which today are called "breakthroughs." They are of the kind which reveal force patterns of universal application in what we have been accustomed to think of as so many different fields of the sciences. In summary, Fuller's thought stream is characterized by: (a) emphasis on dynamics, (b) grasp of synergy as true reality, (c) link to energetic/synergetic geometry, and (d) awareness of underlying pattern in the universe.

IT was now 1956, second year after granting of the first patent in geodesics. Government and business were giving evidence of a growing need for geodesics and tensegrity. That year the roll of industrial licensees under Fuller's patent rights climbed to thirty-one, including such diverse interests as Magnesium Products of Milwaukee, Lunn Laminates, Inc., Domestic Film Products Corp., Container Corporation of America, The Firestone Tire and Rubber Company, and Kaiser Aluminum & Chemical, Inc.

Initial impetus was supplied when the United States Marine Corps demonstrated the feasibility of moving lightweight geodesic domes to advance bases by helicopter. This could be done without taking the domes apart, for the helicopters were able to pick them off the ground at one place and put them down at another, ready for immediate use. Time for erection: zero. These Marine Corps domes were stronger, larger and otherwise more satisfactory than tents. In the scheme of military logistics, they could displace both the tents of advance bases and also the more permanent structures of intermediate supply bases. They could be first to arrive, for speed, and after that could remain, for permanence.

Impetus derived also from the suitability of the geodesic dome for transport and erection at distant sites in far northern territories to house electronic systems for hemisphere defense. For this purpose, structures of geodesic form were made from translucent plastic. Their components were molded into plastic pans. The flanged edges of the pans were color-coded for bolting together in the particular way that would bring physical realization of the great circle integrity which is the essence of the system now known simply as "geodesics." The first hemisphere defense system, housed within a far-flung chain of these plastic geodesic domes, called

46

Radomes, is the one commonly referred to as the DEW (distant early warning) LINE. It reaches from Cape Lisburne, Alaska, to Baffin Island, 3,000 miles of electronic ears. A second defense system, similarly housed in geodesic domes, is furnished by BMEWS (ballistic missiles warning system).

Requests for licenses under Fuller's geodesic patents came from manufacturers wishing to supply the government with Radomes or Marine Corps shelters. Such was the starting spur to a broadening use of geodesics. But this was preceded by the work of a small group of architects and engineers who had been inspired by Fuller's teaching. In university classrooms at North Carolina State, Tulane and Harvard (and elsewhere), students had been acquiring fundamentals of the new geometry and learning its application by designing and building on campuses geodesic domes in as wide a diversity of forms as its geometry and their own imaginations might contrive.

The quality of Fuller's teaching was such that a number of his students were inspired to make of geodesics a life work. This group of students soon became, in effect, a practicing school of architects, a small but earnest coterie who were able to speak the new language of geodesics and synergy, and who had the capability of translating this language into architectural reality. In time, and with their teacher's own encouragement and financial backing, these graduate student groups founded design centers for geodesic construction which emerged corporately as Geodesics, Inc., and Synergetics, Inc., of Raleigh, North Carolina, and Geometrics, Inc., of Cambridge, Massachusetts.

The Raleigh group, led by James M. Fitzgibbon, was encouraged to concentrate its primary effort in the commercial applications of geodesic architecture, and was responsible for designing and supervising the erection of the largest freespan structures ever built, two railroad roundhouses for repair and maintenance of rolling stock of the Union Tank Car Company, the first erected at Baton Rouge, Louisiana,

47

the second at Wood River, Illinois. Domes built of steel plates and tensile struts, these were buildings so vast as to be capable of enclosing the largest football stadium—playing field, spectator stands and all. But so light and thin in relation to their vast proportions that their shells are thinner than that of an eggshell in relation to the egg.

The Cambridge group, led by William Wainright, concentrated much of its early work on designing for the nation's defense establishment, and was responsible for calculating the spherical geometry of the plastic domes for electronic defense networks. This, as we have seen, was instrumental in spreading interest in geodesics across a wide spectrum of United States industry, which in turn created a demand for patent licenses under the rights held by Fuller. Patent Divisions of the Army, Navy and Bureau of Aeronautics, and patent law firms representing some of the largest corporations, subjected Fuller's patents to the most searching investigation before permitting the government to approve or the corporate clients to pay modest royalties for the right to use the patented inventions. It is to be doubted whether any other patent situation has ever been subjected to closer scrutiny by the government which granted the patents, or by a more impressive roster of patent counsel asked to advise their corporate clients, than in the case of those ordered to investigate and advise whether Fuller's patent rights should be respected. A leading patent lawyer, long regarded as dean of the Chicago patent bar, confided to the author that in his practice which extended over half a century, he never had had the privilege of reading a more original and impressive document than the fundamental geodesics patent of Buckminster Fuller. "I am advising my client to take a license," he concluded.

A concomitant of the demand for licenses was a need for the engineering skills of the men and organizations who had become practicing experts in the new field. And so, if the defense establishment of the nation was ready for geodesics, it can be recorded that geodesics was ready for the nation. The specifications, once written, could be met almost head on with designs ready for the building. Before long, streams of plastic Radome components were winging their way to Arctic outposts, ready to stand against icy gales and hostile intentions alike. Other streams were flowing to the Marine Corps.

Alertness to the potential boons promised by the new architecture was not confined to the government and defense, for the year 1956 also saw activity in the world of commercial building. Under license from Fuller, Kaiser Aluminum envisioned and designed a geodesic structure incorporating added features created by its own engineers. This was an aluminum dome which could be tailored to a variety of purposes, and which the Kaiser organization produced and erected for banks, factories, theaters, shopping centers, sports arenas and other uses.

IN contemplating the *modus operandi* of the mind of the inventor, it will be useful to consider what was the preoccupation of that mind during the year 1956 that we have just watched go by with its procession of flying Marine Corps shelters, defense lines of Radomes, and theaters, banks, and arenas. To what extent might Fuller's inventive urge be distracted by the burgeoning success of "the dome"? A less dynamic mind might be likely to find its course magnetized in the direction that fame was taking, but not Fuller's. For him, 1956 was only the beginning of an inventive stream of wider implications in synergetic building construction spreading beyond the dome. This stream was to include tensile integrity trusses useful for rectangular buildings as well as domes, "suspension" buildings, and structures stressed so purely in tension that the minimal compression elements would not even touch one another for transmission of loads. Even undersea islands, anchored "tetrahedrally" in accordance with the form discovered by energetic/synergetic geometry as the first identifiable system in the universe. The deep current of Fuller's thought was too strong to feel influence from temporal advantage. As the licensing royalties flowed in, they were as quickly distributed among those who had shown their willingness to plight their faith with Fuller's. The money went back into the business that had made geodesics ready for the needs of a nation, that of Fuller's former students, then executives in the architectural and manufacturing companies that continued to be the spearheads for testing and introducing the inventor's most advanced concepts in the geodesics field.

The broadening stream of invention was signalled by the filing in 1956 of Fuller's application to patent "synergetic" building construction. The patent was granted in 1961.[5] How

---

[5]United States patent No. 2,986,241, granted May 30, 1961.

could the benefits of geodesic dome construction be extended to more conventional building forms based on the rectangular prism rather than on the sphere? Was there a synergy of forces that could go beyond that discovered within the sphere's great circles? We have learned about the tetrahedron, the geometric figure having four equal equilateral faces. And Fuller has explained that this is a system having applications so wide and varied as to be thought universal. Now Fuller examines the octahedron, which displays eight equal equilateral faces. According to the new invention, both octas and tetras are combined to make a truss system in which these two kinds of geometric figures are congruent. Fuller found that "if any flat roof, wall or floor framework is built up of struts (or sheets) of equal length in such a fashion that such elements are comprised within a common octahedron-tetrahedron system, the strength of the framework is far greater than would be predictable using any conventional formulae based on resolution of forces and known values of strength of materials."[6] So, Fuller continues, "In fact, my practical tests have shown that the actual strength of these flat one system octahedron-tetrahedron structures so far exceeds calculated values as to suggest a hypothesis that such structures are 'synergetic' in the sense that we have a stress behavior in the system which is unpredicted by its parts."

Unpredicted, synergetic, a structure now known as the "Octet truss" or simply, "Octetruss," *oct* for octahedron, *tet* for tetrahedron. It is a system made up of four unique sets of parallel, symmetrically oriented, omni-triangulated planes. For simplicity, we can say, four unique planes. There is a singleness in the system which allows it to carry through the roof, floor and wall sections of a building in a manner akin to a crystalline growth. A servicing dock for a B-26 bomber

---

[6]*Cf.* page 44, *supra,* where a discovery to like effect was reported by Fuller in reference to synergy of the Kabul dome.

51

constructed according to this invention would have a weight of only 0.115 pounds per cubic foot of space enclosed, and when the parts of the dock are disassembled, they will pack for shipment into 1/350th of its ultimate cubic enclosure.

It could now be seen that Fuller's plan of turning the energies of the universe to greatest human advantage extended beyond limitation in form or shape of a building. As the cube did not restrict his thinking, neither did the sphere. The tetrahedron had proved to be a least common denominator of prismatic and spherical structures. As with his mathematics which came before, the ultimate significance of Fuller's inventions lay in universality of application. It was not the visible shape that counted, so much as it was the dynamics of a far more sophisticated concept. Not just a dome or a truss as such, but a complex whose structural stress behavior as a whole was truer to the underlying dynamics of all creation. A structure which, regardless of the materials that went into it, was compounded much of energy and synergy, little of material. In a meaningful sense, it could be called a structure made of energetic/synergetic geometry. Here we are thinking generically both of Fuller's geodesic dome and his octetruss, which, though not visibly alike to any eye but a mathematician's, are bonded by pattern of stress behavior and a common philosophy of conserving material resources through tapping energy sources. Statically unalike. Dynamically alike. In life itself, energy of motion is the universal equation; the material is of lesser significance. For the material can be transformed, while the energy lives on. Fuller's thought patterns never were disassociated from the universal equation.

FOLLOWING his discovery of a structural equation which brings buildings of visual dissimilarity into an energetic/synergetic likeness, Fuller came upon another discovery of a most unexpected nature. He had been experimenting with constructing domes made of plywood. It occurred to him that it might not be necessary to cut the sheets of plywood into triangular shape before fastening them together into a geodesic dome. Why not just use the flat rectangular sheets in their common four-foot by eight-foot form, simply letting them overlap as they might while following a pattern in which the centerlines of the sheets would be aligned with the great circle-based three-way gridding of geodesics? When he tried this, and fastened the sheets together where their corners overlapped, an amazing transformation took place. A pair of triangles, together making a diamond, formed themselves within the rectangular outline of each plywood sheet! The triangles had not been there before. Fuller had not made them. They simply emerged out of nowhere—or from Nature as is usually the case where that kind of a "nowhere" is concerned. The dome had in some natural way made its own geodesic struts—a "self-strutted" dome, as it was named in the patent.[7] The flat sheets had, by pure self-inductive action, become geodesic. They became, Fuller announced, "both roof and beam, both wall and column, and in each case the braces as well." Further explaining his discovery in the patent disclosure, Fuller said:

> They (the flat sheets) become the weather-break and its supporting frame or truss all in one. The inherent three-way grid of cylindrical struts causes the structure as a whole to act almost as a

---

[7]United States patent No. 2,905,113, granted September 22, 1959.

membrane in absorbing and distributing loads, and results in a more uniform stressing of all of the sheets. The entire structure is skin stressed, taut and alive. Dead weight is virtually non-existent. Technically, we say that the structure possesses high tensile integrity in a discontinuous compression system.

Again perception of the "aliveness" of synergetic building. Again Fuller's strong urge to discover optimum tensile integrity. In this instance, the tensile integrity had literally sprung into self-manifestation. The inventor had aimed the sheets in the direction of a geodesic pattern, and—lo and behold—the final pattern had emerged by itself. It was almost as though he had only to suggest to the plywood sheets that they were laid up icosahedrally, and that they had answered, "So we must fall into a full geodesic pattern." Or simply, "We want to be geodesic." (Like the dome that Fuller said "wants" to stand up, and the conventional building that doesn't.) A comprehensive truth had asserted itself. It had spoken spontaneously, for not even in his most excited imagination had Fuller foreseen that triangular strutting was going to appear by inherent geodesic force reaction.

Yet once discovered, such inherent force reaction is demonstrable in an extremely simple way. For the demonstration, it is necessary only to grasp an ordinary three-inch by five-inch file card by the tips of the fingers, two fingers of one hand touching the corners at one end of the card, and two fingers of the other hand touching the corners at the other end. Then the four corners of the card are urged downward and slightly toward one another. The triangles will at once display themselves to view in the form of rounded fold lines. This rather oversimplified demonstration does not reach the sophistication of Fuller's discovery as related to geodesic patterning, but it will serve to explain what is meant by the term "self-strutted." Self-triangling.

The overall pattern of triangles that is distinctive of geo-desics could be made from rectangles. And from what else? If a structure somehow had been programmed to produce a pattern of triangles from rectangular sheets, what might be the possibility of having the same programming create its progeny of triangles from sheets of still other forms? From his discovery up to that point, Fuller knew that the rectangular "file cards" would work, but if not triangular to start with, need they be rectangular? What was the broadest range of possibilities? This kind of extrapolation was instinctive with Fuller, so that he quickly realized that the genus of his invention definitely was not the rectangle. The rectangle was a special case. No, the genus would necessarily be a flat sheet of no particular shape. Formless, an amoeba. Spontaneously his pencil traced a shapeless blob on the paper napkin spread out on the table to explain to his patent lawyer the esoterics of self-strutted buildings. "The starting sheets could be leaf-shaped, any shape at all," said Fuller. His lawyer pursued the wrong end of the sentence, momentarily entranced by the thought of a leaf-shape, and losing the emphasis on "any shape." "What interesting effects would be possible by using special shapes such as leaves!" exclaimed the lawyer. Patient in reproof, Bucky, the teacher, replied in a voice of almost caressing softness, "We are not interested in 'effects,' now are we?" Well there it was, a clear lesson in the motivation of a mind such as Fuller's. Naturally that mind could not be concerned with effects as such. The effects could not be sought.[8]

Yet we can imagine that the architecture produced through comprehensive thought should perforce be pleasing for the eye to see. This for the very reason that it expresses Fuller's thesis of turning the energies of the universe

---

[8]"I have shunned the daily recurrent opportunities to exploit the Energetic-Synergetic geometry as . . . objets d'art." Fuller, Tensegrity, Portfolio & Art News Annual, No. 4, 1961, p. 121.

to human advantage. Natural, therefore inherently pleasing. At any rate, the teaching now is crystal clear. The overlapping sheets could be of any shape imaginable, or of assorted shapes, and the part of nature that is geodesics will make them bend into triangles whose edges create a geodesic form that is strong, stable, and synergetic.

Later in the day of the lesson that geodesic design should never concern itself with "effects," we were privileged to accompany Fuller on a visit to a prototype self-strutted dome. It was one which was designed to serve as a farmhouse and was located in the vicinity of an Iowa village, Van Meter, perhaps an hour's drive west of Des Moines. The visit came on a cold day that eased the mercury twelve degrees below zero, and the domical shell of the farmhouse-to-be rose stark and frozen from a powder blanket of snow. But not stark really, for the sheer symmetry of its geodesic form made it at once a thing of beauty and as much at home on the bleak landscape as an igloo on an ice floe—to which it indeed bore resemblance. The door opening was just that, for no door had been hung in it, and you recoiled an instant from stepping into inside cold. But once in, a surprising breath of warm air brought a welcome caress to frosted faces. "How in the world can it be so warm in here?" you thought, glancing back at the open doorway and hearing the wind. At the far side, opposite, a tiny New Perfection oil stove was unconvincing although there was a bit of a flame within.

"So," said Bucky, answering the unspoken question, "You see why the Eskimo builds his house in the round." Then to make the demonstration complete, "Stand here inside the doorway." We did. "Now extend your hand slowly toward the opening—first take off your glove—and tell me when it feels cold." Six inches inside the opening, warm. In the plane of the missing door, freezing cold. "The explanation?" asked the inventor, "Well, what happens is, that inside of a dome the warm air rises to the apex and then, cooling, slides down along the sloping walls until it reaches the floor. This descending air, still warm though cooling, forms a warm curtain which maintains a surprising integrity as it passes down across the door opening, influenced more by the natural convection currents inside than by the wintry blasts outside." This added virtue of the dome has earned appreciation by the personnel of bases in polar regions where the geodesic dome has been used to advantage. It should be stated, parenthetically, that such use stemmed from recognition of lightness and ease of transport by air. That the dome could be heated so efficiently was simply an extra dividend.

Turning from the still cold-looking doorway which our minds now saw warmly curtained, eyes were lifted to the apex of the dome with much the same magnetism that one experiences as his spirit soars upward to the groined ceiling of a Gothic cathedral. A geodesic dome always surprises with a sense of its immensity. This Iowa farmhouse was a 42-footer, no more (42 feet in diameter at its hemispheric base), but it was overpowering in its seeming vastness. As in the cathedral, spirits soared and we stood in a world apart from the Iowa winter.

BY the spring of 1958, the number of Fuller's licensees had risen to sixty-one. A company called Plydomes, Inc., had been formed to produce the self-strutted dome. In 1959, Fuller filed for a patent on an invention entitled, "Tensile-Integrity Structures." Study of the previous inventions in geodesic structures shows that "tensile integrity" is a term that had been used from the beginning to describe a principal characteristic of such structures. It meant continuity in the pattern of tension forces throughout a structure. Tension was relied on more, compression less. More pull, less push, and therefore greater use of what is best in structural materials —their strength to resist pull. What was most significant about the 1959 invention was not that it was named for tensile integrity, but that it was a comprehensive, daring exploration of the outer limits of tensile force availability in architecture. How fully could man avail himself of the rich store of tensile strength in his new materials? How pure a tension structure could be contrived? How far could we go in the direction of eliminating compression altogether? The tensile integrity invention provides the answers. Also it has the capability of revealing visual manifestations of its use of tension, or more accurately some aspects of such use. This capability is demonstrated when the tensile network of a structure is physically constituted in the form of wires, for the wires are easily understood to be stressed purely in tension. So in this sense we "see" the tension.

A first look at a dome or sphere made according to the invention can be deceptive, for it may not be noticed that the minor elements of the structure, the compression struts, are not actually in contact with one another (discontinuous compression). One does see much of the now familiar geodesic pattern, the triangles, hexagons and pentagons of the icosa progenitor, and the uniformity of its non-polarized design. A closer look, and a first new aspect appears in the strange, "spikey" form that provides a clue to "discontinuous compression." The spikes are the ends of the compression struts all of which are out of touch with one another. Now the significance of the network of wires is perceived, and one discovers that those struts seem just to float in the lacey net of wires. This is a baffling moment, for the mind has difficulty in comprehending why the net of wires does not collapse like a fishnet with its catch of fish, the floating struts. What keeps it all standing, as though it had an impervious skin and gas inside to make it a balloon? The fact that it did stand brought dawning realization that Fuller had accomplished a farther-reaching breakthrough in the optimum use of tensile force.

"The essence of my invention," said Fuller in his tensile integrity patent,[9] "consists in the discovery of how to progressively reduce the aspect of compression in a structure so that, to a greater extent than has been found possible before, the structure will have the aspect of continuous tension throughout and the compression will be subjugated so that the compression elements become small islands in a sea of tension. This is to bring the slenderness, lightness and strength of the suspension bridge cable into the realm previously dominated by the compression column concept of building."

"Small islands in a sea of tension"—what before had been the dead weight of columns and beams brought down at last to the irreducible minimum in the form of these little islands floating in a gossamer web of tensioned wire.

Difficult as it may be to see in the mind that which the eye sees only as a building "standing" mysteriously on an apparently unsupported flexible maze of wires, this is only part of the problem of bringing the total complex within reach of ordinary comprehension. For the rest, we must at-

---

[9]United States patent No. 3,063,521, granted November 13, 1962.

tend to Fuller's explanation of why it is that what the eye sees as a single island is functionally not *one* island but *two*. Yes, this means that there are twice as many functioning compression islands than are to be counted when one adds up the total number of struts present in the structure.

"My tensegrity structure," said Fuller, "comprises struts arranged in groups of three, overlapped to make a tripod as in an Indian tepee." Unlike the tepee, the struts do not touch one another where they overlap. These three struts are the three axes of our old friend, the octahedron. When wires join together the six ends of the three struts, an octahedron is formed. The octahedron comprises the "primary system" as one component of the tensile integrity complex. This primary system is visible only to the mind's eye. First, because when one primary system is joined to a second, an octa axis (strut) of one is *physically* connected to an octa axis (strut) of the other. As the complex is expanded to include additional primary systems, all the axes are so interconnected. Second, because in the total tensegrity complex the wires which otherwise would have made visible six of the twelve edges of each octahedron are *physically* omitted.

Here we have two realities which the mind sees, but the eye cannot; and one unreality which the eye sees, but the mind should not. So strange a state of affairs deserves closer study:

The physical joining of struts of adjacent primary systems (the tepees) is described by Fuller as creating " 'apparent' compressional continuity." Actually the struts so joined apparently into one are functionally two, because the tension wires of one tepee pull in one direction away from the center of the strut that is visually one, and those of the other tepee pull in an opposed direction away from the center of the same strut. Thus one end of that strut acts functionally as one compression column, while its other end acts as another compression column. Two separately acting columns in one "apparent" column. The "apparent" column is therefore said to be in "discontinuous compression." A second aspect of discontinuous compression lies in the physical separation of one pair of physically joined struts from another pair of physically joined struts. This the eye *can* see. But the first it cannot.

And as to the visual obscurity of the primary octa system by reason of the possibility of omitting tension wires which if present would lie along six of the twelve edges of each octahedron, the inventor tells us:

> The omission of such wires tends to obscure the visual appearance of the eight triangular faces of the octahedron, but does not destroy the octahedral aspect of the primary system that is necessarily fixed and predetermined by the presence in the system of the aforesaid six vertexes which characterize the octahedron.

It all adds up this way:
Realities which the mind sees, but the eye cannot—

    a. Two functioning struts in what physically looks like one.
    b. Functioning octa systems in a complex which does not physically reveal complete octas.

An unreality which the eyes sees, but the mind should not—

    c. A strut that is physically one, but functionally is two.

It will be recognized that (c) is the converse of (a), but completeness of analysis demands statement of both. The reason is that in (c) the eye actually sees an unreality, whereas in (a) there was only the failure to see reality.

So what the mind sees in the tensile integrity structure

of this patent, while invisible, contains more of the true reality than what the eye sees. Conversely, in one particular what the eye sees in that same structure is in fact unreality. The "real" is understood to be the unreal, and the invisible to be the true reality.

Where such is the quality of invention that its physical embodiment makes invisible its functional capabilities, of what avail is the pictorial representation of the physical embodiment? If pictures can be so misleading as to make us see something that is not real while failing to make visible what it is that makes the invention work, we have the case where words are better than pictures for explaining that invention. Or, as suggested in the beginning, perhaps even better than pictures explained.

It will be of interest here to observe the difficulty experienced by the patent examiner in Washington when faced with the challenging assignment of analyzing and acting upon Fuller's application for his tensile integrity patent. The examiner, studying the patent drawings, apparently found his mental vision obscured by his physical vision. So much so that at first he misunderstood the meaning of the accompanying explanation of the invention, and afterward disbelieved the explanation, evidently having had his mind too far clouded by what he had seen in the drawings. Here then was an example of the problem noticed in the beginning, of how best to explain the discoveries of Fuller when we understand that they probe so deeply into the unseen dynamics of force and motion. In the case of the patent examiner whose only difficulty was that he had allowed his visual perceptions to cloud those of his mind, the simple solution was to suggest that he lay aside the patent drawings and listen to a fresh explanation of the unseeable aspects of the invention, starting all the way back with that primary tensegrity, the octahedron. Soon the examiner found his mind soaring into the realities of the largely invisible but very real world of tensile integrity structuring, and the patent was granted.

On one occasion Fuller was invited to be a special guest speaker at a meeting of The Patent Office Society, an organization of the active examiners of the United States Patent Office where the meeting was held. The officers of the Society stated that Professor Fuller was the first inventor who had ever been asked to address the examiners at such a convocation insofar as their records showed, and was certainly the first to be so honored within their memory. The meeting was in the afternoon, and the examining staff was given time off so that if they chose they might avail themselves of the opportunity to hear the illustrious inventor. There was a record attendance of over eight hundred examiners. Obviously entranced by Fuller's zeal as he led their trained minds deep into his own philosophical approach to invention and patents, the seats of the government auditorium across the street from the Patent Office were still filled two and a half hours later, although it was then well past working hours. As Fuller concluded his address, a score of examiners pressed eagerly around him. Among them were two who were responsible for acting on certain Fuller applications then pending. Each of these in turn identified the invention described in the case he was handling, asked a question or two about it, and concluded with assurances that an early allowance of Fuller's claims could be expected. Fuller had unwittingly become his own skillful advocate before the Patent Office. He possessed a firm grasp of the requirements of the patent law for patentability. Aware that an invention to be entitled to the patent grant must be unobvious, he had as a rule been alert to inform his patent counsel whenever an invention of his brought results that he had not expected. Such a result he would always refer to as a "surprise."

The patent examiners generally were impressed by Fuller's surprises. But these same examiners, and those of other patent offices round the world, used to have quite a problem in becoming accustomed to Fuller's new vocabulary of geodesics. Although the vocabulary was one that had become the everyday working language of practicing experts, and was familiar to students in Fuller's university classes on virtually every major campus in the United States and those of many nations and on all the continents, it was yet too early to expect to find the new words in the recognized dictionary sources. So, many examiners were unready to tolerate the language even though reminded that it is settled law that "an inventor is his own lexicographer." In the end, most had to acknowledge that new art must create new language. Today, that new language has become essential semantics not only to the mathematician and architect, but also the accepted language of the patents in the field.

SOON after his invention of tensile integrity structuring, Fuller became intrigued with the possibility that his lightweight geodesic structures might be made lighter still. Monsanto Chemical Company had been attracted by the self-strutted dome. As it could be made of flat plywood sheets, the company foresaw a new use for its polystyrene laminates. These comprised a core of expanded polystyrene faced with sheets of paperboard or plastic. With such styrofoam laminates it should be feasible to construct feather-light geodesic domes. They would be useful as shelters for many purposes, for example as low-cost "on site" warehouses in the building construction field.

Probing for the optimum in simplicity, Fuller conceived in the spring of 1960, a geodesic dome that was well suited to the Monsanto venture. It could be built with the use of just two kinds of panel components, each of diamond shape, and appeared to represent the ultimate in simplicity of design, parts stocking and erection. Also, it possessed the advantage of being "truncatable," meaning that it was adapted to making a shelter of selectively variable height according to particular needs. At one height it would be in the form of one half of a sphere. For less height, it would have the form of three-eights of a sphere, for greater, five-eighths. The feature was that whichever the line of truncation that might be selected, the ground line of the building will be straight. This was accomplished through a special design of the spherical geometry of the dome which brings edges of the diamond-shaped panels into aligment at each of the three lines of truncation. Hence there is no need to provide special foundation line "filler" panels as would otherwise be the case. The same geometry created also the further simplicity of componentation which narrowed the number of panel types to two, as stated.

The secret of the geometry lies in the relationships between the lengths of the sides of the diamonds and between their long and short axes. These relationships are expressed as chord factors. Six diamond panels are so grouped that the vertexes of the acute angles at one end of the long axis of each meet at a common point, three of the six sections of the group having the following chord factors:

Sides adjacent said acute angles	= 0.42
Remaining sides	= 0.33
Short axis of the diamond	= 0.38

and the other three of the six sections being alternated with the first three sections and having the following chord factors:

Sides adjacent the acute angles	= 0.42
Short axis of diamond	= 0.44
Long axis of diamond	= 0.71

These are the particular relationships which yield both truncatability and two-component simplicity. No theory need be suggested to explain why this is so, for here the mathematics did not sire the invention. Instead, the invention discovered the mathematical formula, empirically. This is remarkable because it shows again the pervasive influence of Fuller's mathematical mind. Even if mathematics was not progenitor of the invention, this circumstance did not preclude him from finding a way to define it by arithmetic formula.

The patent for this invention[10] is of special interest for another reason, as it affords a penetrating example of Fuller's sensitive awareness of reality in what cannot be seen. So sensitive is his awareness in this instance that it enables him

---

[10]United States patent No. 3,203,144, granted August 31, 1965.

to discover a fact that is in direct opposition to that which our eyes, in error, would make us believe to be true. This is disclosed in the inventor's analysis of the phenomenon of truncatability. He observes that two of the lines of truncation *look* like what are known as "lesser" circles (as opposed to great circles) such as the lesser circles comprised in the parallels of latitude of a standard globe in which the equator and the meridians are the only great circles. Yet in the dynamics of geodesics these two lines of truncation are not the lesser circles they would appear to be. Functionally, they are chordal modules (parts) of *great* circles. Fuller demonstrates this through a brilliant probe into the geometry of the spherical icosahedron. In characteristic manner, he instinctively returns to the genesis of geodesics and infallibly drives through to the true dynamics of its truncatable form:

> Particular attention is directed to the fact that the chordal modules of the lines of truncation, when viewed in one aspect, appear to be chordal modules of lesser circles. However, by construction upon the spherical icosahedron wherein all of the vertexes, and therefore both axes, of the diamond panels lie in great circle planes, these chordal modules in reality lie in planes passing through the center of the sphere whose intersections with the sphere describe great circle arcs. The phenomenon of alignment of panel edges for truncation may be described as the ancillary appearance of small circles, which may be likened to the parallels of latitude of a standard globe of the earth, at the three-eights and five-eighths lines of truncation occurring, however, as incidents of true great circle, i.e. geodesic, construction.

So the unapparent great circle modules are dynamically real, and the "apparent" lesser circles are unreal in geodesics (albeit real in the sense of ancillary availability for base line truncation). Or at least the "apparent" is real only in the sense of visual statics. Fuller's mind, intuitively or through practice as the case may be, unerringly searches out the total of reality in terms of the dynamics of universe. His mind's eye does not let him be fooled by his optic nerves.

AN added catalyst to the widening of Buckminster Fuller's vision during the 1950s and 1960s was provided by the stepped-up tempo of his travels. Everywhere in swift succession there were classes to be taught and speaking engagements to be met. The demands on his time were multiplied to the extreme so that sometimes, after flying half round the world, he would be addressing one meeting in the afternoon, another in the evening and a third the following day. When the third happened to be in another city, the schedule could become a little rigorous even for Fuller! If anyone could "fill the unforgiving minute with sixty seconds worth of distance run," Fuller was Kipling's man.

Could else be needed to give his mind the comprehensive touch, it was furnished by a galloping world perspective as daily he touched the minds of others all round Earth's compass. These others included persons of many callings, for Fuller's teaching was sought not alone by scientific and architectural groups, but also by businessmen, economists, lawyers, doctors, educators and statesmen alike. From his own United States to distant India, from Japan to South Africa, Fuller labored on, and grew in the esteem and affection of all whose minds he touched. His were the diverse roles of college professor and personal confidant of leaders of state. Meanwhile he called unceasingly on strong reserves of energy as he met ever tightening schedules of work and travel, forever eager to feed the imaginations of all who were striving for new understanding and purpose.

As Fuller taught, he also listened. As he listened, he translated. As he translated, the scope of his teaching grew. The effect was regenerative as the teacher's mind responded to the expanding thought pattern of the student. Fuller describes this sort of response as "positive feed-back," the process by which one idea fed into his mind from any observed or translated experience of man generates a family of related ideas from which a broader generalization of the beginning idea emerges. All of us possess to a greater or less extent this capability of developing the general from the specific, and of being aided in the process by interchange of ideas with others. With Fuller, the regenerative process plays a peculiarly dominant role. How the process works in his comprehensive thought climate is disclosed by a case history. The history is one which will reveal also something of the incredible tempo of Fuller's inventing.

As 1961 became the new year, Fuller conceived his invention of the suspension building. He himself recounts the facts leading up to the invention:[11]

> On or about December 20, 1960, I received by cable an invitation from Mr. Shoriki, Chairman, Nippon Television Network Corporation, to come to Japan for the purposes of (1) studying the possibility of constructing an indoor baseball stadium, and (2) making popular lectures on the United States modern architecture in Tokyo, Osaka, Sapporo and other several cities in Japan. This was confirmed by a formal letter invitation received immediately before Christmas. A similar invitation was received by my associate, Shoji Sadao of New York City, on December 26, 1960.
>
> My first thoughts related to the idea for my invention came to me during the first contemplation of a possible trip to Japan, and took form in my mind only after receiving the invitation before Christmas of 1960.
>
> Then, during the Christmas holidays, namely between Christmas and New Year's, I conceived my

---

[11]The quotations are from the inventor's affidavit to The United States Patent Office.

invention substantially as disclosed in the forms illustrated in Figs. 4, 5 and 7 of my patent application. ... These concepts even then were only worked out in my mind, but I decided that the subject matter was of such interest and promise that I would want to make a disclosure thereof when I reached Tokyo. So I immediately got in touch with my associate, ... Shoji Sadao, by long distance telephone and described my mental concept to him with the request that he prepare sketches with all possible speed for the use of my attorney in preparing a patent application. This disclosure to Mr. Sadao was accomplished within a matter of possibly one, two or three days after conception and between Christmas Day 1960 and New Year's Day 1961.

Fuller had transmitted an understanding of his invention from Los Angeles to New York by a telephone call made within at most "three days" after conception. Then, Fuller continues,

During the ensuing period between New Year's Day 1961 and January 19, 1961, the concept continued to fulminate and on or about January 19, 1961, I conceived the embodiment of my invention as represented in Figs. 18 and 19 of my application for patent and disclosed it to my patent attorney by telephone call made from Texarkana, Texas, to New York City. Other forms as depicted in Figs. 1, 2, 3 and 8-17 inclusive, were conceived in the period between January 9, 1961 and January 19, 1961.

On January 9, 1961, Fuller's associate, Shoji Sadao, furnished Fuller's patent attorney a first disclosure of the invention including preliminary sketches showing a number of

71

its embodiments. At the same time the attorney was told that Fuller was going to leave for Tokyo where he expected to arrive early in February and to be called upon to make at once a full disclosure there, most probably of a public nature. This anticipated chain of events created a pressing legal problem, because, under Japanese law, a public disclosure of invention before the filing of a patent application would preclude valid patenting in Japan. But if within the limited time remaining before Fuller's scheduled arrival in Tokyo an application could be prepared, signed and placed on file in the United States, the problem would be solved. For by treaty[12] the United States filing date could be claimed as the effective filing date of an application filed in Japan within a year afterward.

The race to place a complete specification and formal patent drawing in Fuller's hands for signing before his plane would be taking off for Japan was hampered by the circumstance that Fuller was then in California, his attorney in New York City. On January 9, the same day that the disclosure was received by the attorney, sketches for patent drawings were made. Also on that same day these sketches were sent by wirephoto to Fuller, then in flight between Los Angeles and San Francisco.

Among the wirephotos there were included sketches of a number of additional embodiments of the invention born of analysis of the inventor's disclosure by the attorney and his patent draftsman. The draftsman[13] was an accomplished artist whose mind was acutely sensitive in its responsiveness to the underlying currents of Fuller's thoughts and philosophy. Quick to sense the generic thrust of the invention, he created in dry point several alternate forms that the disclosure brought to his mind. These were the additional em-

---

[12]The International Convention for the Protection of Industrial Property.
[13]Richard Stankiewicz, Professor of Art, State University of New York at Albany and Artist-in-residence, Amherst College.

bodiments which have been referred to as being included in the wirephotos transmitted to Fuller for approval.

Upon the inventor's examination of the photos, there occurred the feed-back of his original idea, expanded to test scope of invention insofar as could be imagined by draftsman and attorney. The result, as Fuller said, was that "Other forms [of the invention] were conceived in the period between January 9, 1961 and January 19, 1961." These other forms went distances beyond anything discoverable by visual examination of the wirephotos. They were the direct product of feed-back of intelligence and ensuing gestation by a mind characteristically free from formal knowledge limitations. Reason suggests that it is this freedom which affords to Fuller's mind its increased potential for regenerative action.

On January 19, Fuller's description of the additional forms of his invention reached New York. Within the ensuing twenty-four hours, drawings were made of these forms and the formal patent papers made ready for signing. These were carried by hand to a rendezvous at the mid-continent airport of St. Louis where Fuller was intercepted on a flight from Illinois to the west coast on the first leg of his trip to Tokyo.

As the days and hours were harvested and gleaned of every last minute in the hurry to put the necessary documents into the Washington patent office before the moment of Fuller's arrival in Tokyo, a tiny gap appeared. There had not been enough unforgiving minutes to get all the ink on the patent drawings, so they had to be left partly in pencil. Formal requirements of the patent rules had not been met fully. In the end, the Patent Office waived such requirements as was permitted where sufficiently unusual circumstances warranted. But in sharp contrast of tempo, it took seven months for the Office to grant the waiver. Seven months to decide that Fuller had acted as fast as he should! In a decision by the First Assistant Commissioner of Patents taken May 18, 1961, it was suggested, ". . . no showing has been made in the instant case why the applicant did not authorize the preparation of the application earlier in view of his impending trip to Japan." The Commissioner had managed to overlook the statement made in Fuller's petition that he had ordered preparation of his application within at most three days after conception. Fuller answered simply, "The reason why I did not authorize the preparation of my application at an earlier date than I did, was that I had not made the invention at any earlier date." His petition was granted, and the filing date of January 24, 1961 was awarded. The race to Washington had been won. It was February when Fuller arrived in Tokyo and disclosed his invention to the excited Japanese. His right to patent protection in Japan[14] had been preserved.

And so, against this backdrop of frenzied patent activity, the suspension building was unveiled in a forward-looking Japan. This building was another part of Fuller's tensile integrity frontier. It can be imagined as consisting essentially of an ascending series of rings in the form of curtain walls. Each ring of the series in smaller than the one below it, creating a visual similarity to a pyramid, particularly when the rings are square. Unlike the pyramids of Egyptian antiquity, the upper layers are not piled up on the lower ones. Instead, each succeeding ring is *suspended* from the one below it. The general principle is to run supporting wires or cables from the upper part of a lower ring to the lower part of an upper ring. Following the same system, it is possible to create many different forms of building, including the domical form of the geodesic dome. Fuller said, "I have discovered how to make building structures and components possessing in substantial measure the advantages of catenary suspension heretofore confined principally to the suspension bridge. The catenary cables of the suspension bridge sag downwardly to the mid-point of the bridge, and would seem to possess no utility in any structure which arches upwardly. So it has been

---

[14]And in countries having laws similar to Japan's.

a surprise to me to find that there is a way by which a catenary suspension system can be converted into an arched structure of domical or polygonal form. By breaking up the suspension cables into increments suspending an ascending series of polygonal or circular frames stepped upwardly one within another, altitude is gained, replacing the catenary sag of the bridge cables with a rising, arched, suspension system."[15] So a sort of upside down suspension bridge system becomes a building. Small wonder that the impressionable Japanese were excited.

---

[15]United States patent No. 3,139,957, granted July 7, 1964.

FULLER's translation of building to geometry, or geometry to building, continued. In December of 1961 he filed application to patent[16] what he called "hex-pent" construction, a name easily recognized to be derived from the hexagon and pentagon of the geometer, figures of six sides and five sides. Again there is geodesic construction based on our old friend the spherical icosahedron, comprised of twenty equilateral spherical triangles. Fuller makes certain that our mathematical profundity will be sufficiently deep, as he explains with great care that instead of twenty triangles per sphere there can just as well be the twelve spherical pentagons of the dodecahedron. (The dodeca is the inversion of the icosa.[17])

Not only that, but as a further alternative there can be the thirty spherical diamonds of the tricontahedron, for in the art of geodesics the same division of the sphere results regardless of whether one considers that the breakdown has been based upon the icosahedron, the dodecahedron or the tricontahedron.

Starting, then, with any of these three spherical polygons, a variety of structural forms emerges. Looking unalike one another, the least common denominator of their interrelated energy geometry makes them functionally and dynamically alike. The hexagon furnishes the key to the invention which consists in a framework including six-sided panels, three sides straight, three curved. The three curved sides of adjacent panels form circular openings. Here appears the tensile integrity aspect which is never far from the heart of any of Fuller's inventions in geodesics. In the present instance, it

---

16United States patent No. 3,197,927, granted August 3, 1965.

17Cf. Felix Klein, Elementary Mathematics from an Advanced Standpoint: Arithmetic, Algebra Analysis, translated from 3rd (1925) edition; New York, Dover Publications; p. 123.

arises from the concept of using tension rings which grasp the adjoining panels around the circular openings and draw the panels together into a comprehensive tensile network.

Once more there is the striking simplicity of componentation. With the use of only two primary panel types, panels twenty feet in diameter will produce a dome or sphere 182 feet in diameter. Fuller said, "If we reduce the maximum diameter of the components to 10 feet for practicable delivery by truck, the 12-frequency layout will permit construction of a dome 88 feet in diameter at the 'equator.' Similarly, a 24-frequency layout, using only four main types of components, will permit construction of a dome 176 feet in diameter whose components are of a size to be delivered by conventional motor transport." Thus the mathematics, however profound, find final expression in the most practical results, with even this careful attention to the feasibility of ordinary motor transport to the building site. This characteristic linking of the most sophisticated of mathematical concepts to an awareness of how such concepts can be utilized to man's greatest advantage, furnishes another indication of Fuller's concern with the totality of a problem.

IN the octet truss, Fuller had projected his ideas for tensile gain in architecture beyond the domical form, as the truss was useful for any other form of building as well. Nine years later, he invented another kind of structure that would, with equal facility, make a building that is round or square, tall or flat, a floor or roof, a tower—or, if one wished, a form like a tree. Or just a "no" form that is unlike anything on earth. This was the star tensegrity of 1964, called simply "octahedral building truss." The term "star" derived from the star-like facets of a dome designed and built for a country club in the environs of Tokyo.

Fuller introduced his invention with an analysis of the history of the art of building that after so many long centuries had not reached the point of more than a token tapping of resources in tensile strength of materials. With care, he outlined the whole problem, noticing the immensity of man's neglect of his own discoveries of how to make materials stronger in tension:

Advances in the technology of materials have resulted in the discovery of the means for producing remarkable increases in tensile strength properties of the materials. Noticeably this has been true in the field of metal alloys, ferrous and nonferrous. Materials of great tensile strength have been developed also in plastics. Glass fibers of enormous strength have become available and are widely used. Notwithstanding the general availability of such high tensile properties in materials, comparatively little has been done in the direction of utilizing pure tension elements in building construction. For building purposes, engineers have clung tenaciously to age-old concepts which rely primarily upon the compressive strength of the materials used so that structures have been erected stone upon stone, beam upon column, all with the utilization of a vast deadweight of materials. With the use of the somewhat lighter weight girders now employed, for example, in the construction of floors and roofs of conventional buildings, some increase in the use of the tensile properties of materials has been made, but still relying to a great extent on the presence of large and heavy compression members.

So, said Fuller,

I have found a way of building a truss which allows the use of many elements loaded purely in tension, indeed, one in which such purely tensioned elements predominate, so that relatively few compression members are needed. Further, I have discovered how to do this in a way which provides a smooth surface well adapted to cladding in the construction of floors, roofs and walls, and which is remarkably well adapted to the construction of spherical form buildings inclusive of buildings known as geodesic domes.

How predominant the tension elements were, is shown by the fact that the basic building "block" of the invention[18] was a unit of octahedral form having *twelve* flexible edges capable of being stressed only in pure tension, and just *three* columnar members to act under compression. Fuller explained:

Regarding the fundamental purpose of the invention, it is, of course, of the utmost significance that we have here a ratio between pure tension and pure compression of four to one. (If when six units are interconnected ... only one set of tension elements is used where the congruent faces are found, some of the tension elements will be eliminated and the ratio between tension and compression elements will become three to one.)

---

[18]United States patent No. 3,354,591, granted November 28, 1967.

Four to one or three to one as the case may be, the ascendency of tension to the throne occupied for so long by King Compression is high drama. At long last, builders can begin to realize on the tension potential of a dynamic universe. And it is a universe whose destiny is shaped by the invisible tension network which holds the planets to their celestial orbits. What a pleasing harmony of nature Fuller found in this discovery of a geometrical network of tension that can hold a building erect. Such is the larger frame of reference for the mind of the comprehensivist, Buckminster Fuller.

Chapter 5

UNDERSEA ISLAND

NOW we go back awhile to 1959, for it is not to be supposed that during the years of tensegrity building there was nothing else afoot. Navy man and inveterate sailor that he was, Fuller in 1959 found his thoughts drawn back to the sea. He realized early that more of man's immediate destiny would lie in his efficient use of undersea resources than in his probes to outer space. His mind began to perceive man-livable complexes beneath the oceans, and it formed a concept of undersea islands. How would such islands be anchored? "Tetrahedrally," said he. A recurrent realization that the tetrahedron, that first system identifiable as a primary division of universe, would be the least common denominator—this time between the premises of architectural logic at sea and on land. What made sense on land would make sense under the seas.

The problem was to gain stability of man's future undersea living and working quarters. Also for today's needs in offshore oil drilling rigs, and tomorrow's in manned undersea bases for explorations of the ocean floor, Fuller sought an anchoring system which would effectively restrain an undersea island against unwanted motion, yet which would permit steady movement up and down with the ebb and flow of the tides. The "island," in the case of the well drilling rig, is a submerged caisson within which is installed the derrick and other equipment used in drilling operations. A hollow communications shaft extends from within the caisson to a boarding platform above the surface of the sea. Fuller recognized that arrangements of this kind had been proposed before. He was concerned with finding a more practical anchoring system for the drilling rig.

For this purpose, Fuller conceived a system in which the buoyant caisson is submerged under the pull of anchor rodes extending in several directions. The arrangement of the anchor rodes is of special importance. Several of them extend at a tangent to the body of the caisson to exert their pull in a clockwise direction, while others extend at an opposite tangent so as to exert their pull in a counterclockwise direction. Said Fuller, "The one group of rodes creates a torque which is equal and opposite to that created by the other. This has the result that the caisson is fixed in the grip of opposed torques while yielding to slow vertical movement with the tides against the resilient pull of the catenary sags in the rodes." This gave to Fuller's system what is described in the patent[1] as "three (or more) criss-crossing pairs of rodes distributed so as to extend tangentially away from the sides of the island in several directions."

"Now," said Fuller, "we come to the most exciting aspect of the system. It is *tetrahedral* in form!" Always he would show strong emotional excitement when he was revealing the kinship of one of his inventions to the tetrahedron. This is understandable when we remember about the key role played by the tetra in the geometry of energy and synergy. The tetra, a fundamental system of the universe, here solves a problem of unusual difficulty. It shapes an anchoring pattern capable of accommodating itself comfortably to the turbulent seas, most ancient and respected adversary of man.

"Do you see the tetrahedrons? The anchors for one rode of each pair are the base corners of a tetra whose apex is the undersea island. The anchors of the other rode of each pair define a similar tetra. Now," said Fuller, with mounting zeal,

---

[1]United States Patent No. 3,080,583, granted March 12, 1963.

we have two countertorquing tetrahedra. This arrangement produces vertical stability for our island.

"Again, the 'two-ness' of universe," continued Fuller, falling into his familiar drill pattern that sweeps his listener along with the force of rapid fire semantics. You remembered the revelation of the one spherical triangle that is actually two, one convexly curved, the other concave, so that Fuller's short-hand speech quickly brought the countertorquing tetrahedra into a more comprehensive perspective. Suddenly you experienced a new thoroughness of understanding, an expanding comprehension that you could almost feel within your cerebrum. It was as though the teacher somehow had communicated a measure of his intuitive powers to you, his pupil. Your mind was securely aboard his undersea island, feeling its steadiness, and understanding why.

Chapter 6

TENSILE INTEGRITY BY ELECTRONIC COMPUTER

I

FULLER'S imagination, having spun a tensile web of architecture from the octahedron, turned next to the practical problem of how to manufacture the octahedron itself. This peculiar figure, with its maze of slim wires strung around three axial struts, posed a challenge in production technique. The struts had to be floated in their sea of twelve tension members, and, until the tension net was complete and stressed, there was really nothing to hold the complex in any shape at all. Besides, the three struts had to be held in a criss-crossed arrangement, each at just the right angle to the others and with their vertexial ends correctly disposed to put each of the six vertexes of the octahedron exactly where they should be.

The geometry of the octahedron established the starting point for Fuller's invention of a method and apparatus for spinning octahedral building "blocks" of forms which can be varied at will to meet a wide range of construction needs. The three struts, held in predetermined angular relation, form a preliminary assembly which is rotated while a wire is fed through a guide in such a way as to attach itself to the ends of the struts. Meanwhile, the wire guide is moved to and fro in timed relation to rotation of the strut assembly, bringing the wire sequentially over the several ends of the three struts. By choosing just the right sequence, the wires can be set up to make the twelve edges of a complete octahedron without the need to reverse rotation of the strut assembly. An intriguing aspect of this procedure is that simple two-dimensional movements of the wire guide to and fro in a single plane will result in the production of the three-dimensional octahedron.

Describing his invention, Fuller speaks of the "seemingly complex but truly simple form of the octahedral unit." As man's works conform imperfectly to nature, they possess unnatural complexity, though perhaps seeming to be simple. So deceptive is the semblance of simplicity that often it can be dissembled only upon long studied analysis. To opposite effect, nature shows us much that has an appearance of complexity but which can prove to be basically simple. Take the case of the rectilinear building that "wants to fall down," as Fuller taught us, but which is gusseted against doing so. Such a building is deceptively simple in its rectangular prismatic form—you don't see the gussets, or, if you do, you pay them little heed as you are so well accustomed to them. Then consider the building of geodesic form which instantly suggests a complexity of spherical geometry, but does so only when approached from the rectilinear foundation of Euclidean geometry. This same geodesic form, when observed against the background of Fuller's energetic/synergetic geometry, is easily comprehended as the entrancingly simple fact of nature that it is.

A partner in true simplicity is the octahedron. Even when spun in the form which outlines not only the octahedron but also its three axes, we see more, not less, of octahedral structuring, for the three axes of the octa at once define its unique geometry. What at first may seem only to be a strange array of struts floating in a web of tension wires becomes, upon informed analysis, a simple octahedron, for the web is observed to define the eight triangular faces, twelve edges and six vertexes, while the struts define the three axes, of the octahedron.

During the spinning of the octahedral building unit, data of the correlated movements of the spinner and wire feed guide are stored for "play-back" in the forming of duplicate units. Thus a particular design of unit becomes the progenitor of others of the same species. But more, the play-back programs can be created with the use of electronic computers in which data are stored for a myriad of octahedral variants.

The octahedral building unit is a true member of Fuller's tensegrity family. And here we witness the phenomenon of creation of a tensegrity complex by computer. By this ingenious extrapolation on nature's own tension plan of the universe, Fuller has taken one more step in turning its energies to greater human advantage.

II

IN March of 1965, Fuller filed application in Washington to patent his octa spinning invention. Action on the application was taken by the Patent Office two years later. In a letter dated March 15, 1967, the examiner reported that he had examined the application and had determined that Fuller's claims could not be allowed. His rejection was based, not on anticipation by others, but on his feeling that the invention was obvious from what was shown in a number of previous patents, for these could be so altered and combined one with another as to re-create Fuller's concept. In finding that the method was obvious, the examiner suggested how a 1956 patent for a yarn winding reel might be modified by using it in combination with an indexing operation shown by a patent issued in 1893. Fuller's invention was resubmitted with supporting argument. When, in December of 1967, the claims were rejected for a second time, the inventor's counsel advised him that, "The examiner does not have any reference which anticipates the real concept of the invention," and that it remained to seek a favorable ruling by arranging an oral interview at the Patent Office. If the examiner could not then be persuaded to allow the claims, an appeal would be necessary.

Always Fuller had been successful in obtaining patents for his inventions, although often the difficulties usual to any patent prosecution were the greater because the inventions were of such fundamental nature. It is harder to get a broad patent than a narrow one, and octa spinning was a highly imaginative invention which imposed a breadth of claiming that augured a long, hard battle in Washington. This time, Fuller decided not to accept the burden of prolonging the patent prosecution. So the application was dropped without presentation of oral argument, and there is no way of knowing whether a patent might ultimately have been granted.

Strong motivation for Fuller's patenting program round the world was born of his natural drive to teach, not alone from thoughts of pecuniary advantage to be derived from licensing royalties. He never entered actively into licensing proposals or negotiations, preferring to leave that to his business and legal aides. These he encouraged not to solicit licensees, but only to handle requests for licenses when received, or, when occasion demanded as where there seemed likelihood that someone was preparing to infringe one of his patents, then to call the prospective infringer's attention to the patent, and to the availability of a license. While Fuller did not wish to seek patent profits by "selling" efforts, he was adamant in seeking to forestall efforts of others to profit by making unauthorized use of his inventions. As he made those inventions available to all at reasonable cost, the patents became widely licensed and no need arose to bring action in the courts to enforce them.

The royalties received were plowed back into the businesses of geodesic enthusiasts in Geometrics, Inc., Synergetics, Inc., and Geodesics, Inc., at Cambridge and Raleigh, themselves "teachers" of the geodesic art. Hence in the strictest sense, Fuller's ultimate preoccupation was with education, not profits. The patents, when royalties came, were being used to spread knowledge of the inventions and the gain to others in using them. Besides, the printing of the patents round the world and their distribution to libraries made the inventions better known so that one day when the patents expired all might benefit from their teachings. That this aim in itself formed a significant part of Fuller's philosophy of patenting (as it does in the rationale of government awards of patent monopolies for limited periods of time) may be deduced from the fact that Fuller derived little in the way of royalty return on his foreign patent investment. Yet during three decades he continued to patent his inventions throughout the world. And the true answer is not that his motivation was only the distant prospect of foreign royalties. On one occasion when faced with mounting bills for foreign patent taxes and pressed by counsel's questions about his commercial prospects in some faraway land, Fuller replied, "I believe it is good to have patents in existence everywhere for people to read in the libraries of their own countries and in their own languages." To him there was intrinsic worth in having patents issued and printed, profits or no.

Fuller's decision to forego patenting his octa spinning invention was disappointing to him if only because it meant that no patent would be published. At great personal sacrifice, he had fulfilled a demanding round the world schedule of lecturing and of teaching in the universities. It was his wish that his inventions be described in the libraries of patents. This was another chapter in his one-man teaching saga. And there would be no printed teaching of this invention by any United States patent. Fuller has requested the author to remedy this by publishing his full patent disclosure as a part of the story of his inventions, a story which otherwise would not be as complete as he would like it to be. The full patent specification is given in the succeeding chapter.

III

THE invention relates to the fabrication of building trusses and components.

My United States patent, No. 3,354,591, granted December 7, 1964, describes a truss construction which is capable of utilizing more efficiently the tensile strengths of the materials from which the truss is constructed. In such construction, it has been found possible to use many elements loaded purely in tension, indeed, one in which such purely tensioned elements predominate so that relatively few compression members are needed. The construction is one in which a number of units, conveniently made of criss-crossed struts bound together by a network of tension elements, form the basic components, or "building blocks" used in putting together the truss. While such truss components, once assembled, are self-contained units that are easy to handle, their fabrication can become rather complex due to the fact that they are made up of compression struts which are virtually suspended in a network of wire. During fabrication, it is essential to maintain the proper angular relationship between the criss-crossed struts and the relative dispositions of the ends of the struts for a given predetermined angular relation.

My present invention is concerned with the solution of the particular problems involved in the fabrication of these peculiar strut-and-wire components such as those exemplified in my prior patent aforesaid, and to the means by which such components can be interconnected to form a building truss.

According to one form of my invention, the truss structure produced comprises a number of interconnected three-dimensional components each of which has several struts, and flexible edge portions extending between the ends of the struts to form an initially self-supporting unit. These components are joined together by connecting the ends of the struts of one component to the ends of the struts of adjacent components through partly spherical fastening elements perforated to provide selective adjustment of the angular relationship between the struts of the interconnected components.

Fabrication of the truss components comprises the steps of arranging the struts in predetermined angular relation to one another to form a preliminary strut assembly, rotating the strut assembly, feeding a wire for attachment to the ends of the struts, and producing relative movements between the rotating strut assembly and the wire feed to bring the wire into engagement with first one strut and then another, thus to form flexible edge portions of the truss component. My apparatus includes means for performing these several steps in the desired sequence, and for programming the wire feeding device according to predetermined design patterns for components of varying form.

The invention has particular application to the fabrication of components of octahedral form comprising eight triangular faces. These faces are defined by the wire network, and there are three compression struts which are arranged along the three axes of the octahedron.

Figure 1 depicts a single octahedral component in perspective. Figure 2 is a view of one of the partly spherical fastenings of the same component. Figure 3 is an enlarged detail of an end of one of the struts, with associated wire-fastening means.

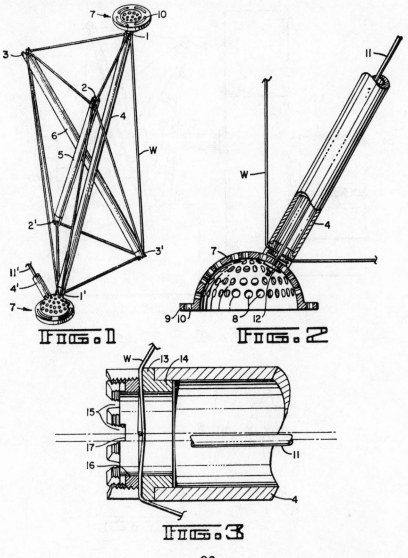

FIG. 1

FIG. 2

FIG. 3

In Figure 4, we see in isometric perspective the apparatus which "spins" the wire onto the struts; in Figure 5 an optional form of means for binding the struts together after the completed octahedral component has been removed from the spinner.

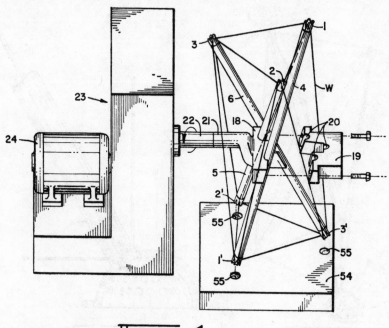

FIG. 4

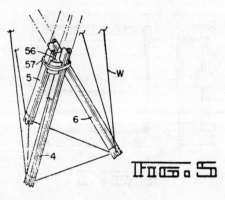

FIG. 5

The isometric perspective of Figure 6 shows not only the spinner of Figure 4, but also the wire feeding means and means for producing relative movements between the rotating strut assembly and the wire feeding means, in combina-

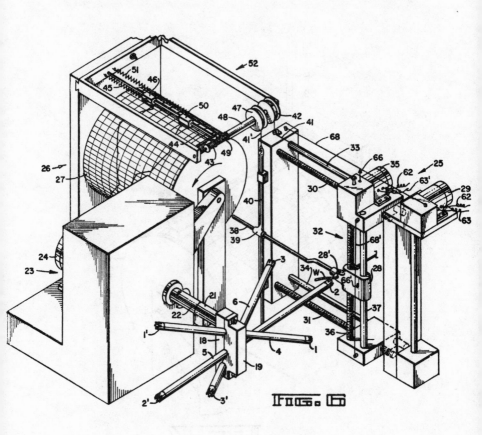

FIG. 6

tion with a programming control means. Figure 7 reproduces a portion of the same apparatus as it appears following removal of the stylus frame of the programmer and substitution of the photoelectric "playback" device.

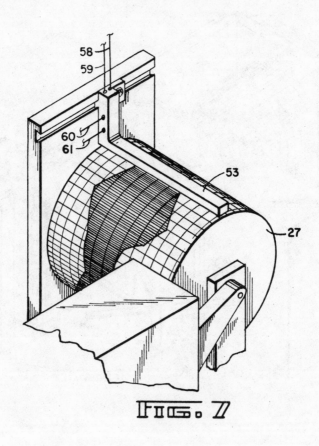

FIG. 7

A diagram of the control circuit for one of the two motors of the wire feed control is furnished by Figure 8, while the diagram of Figure 9 illustrates the special case in which the truss component is a regular octahedron.

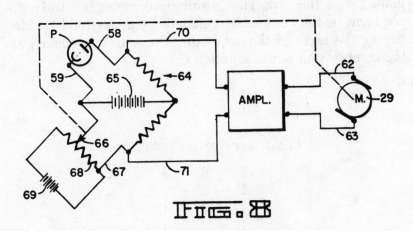

FIG. 8

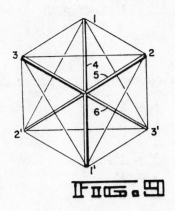

FIG. 9

Looking first at Figure 1, we see an octahedral truss component which has three compression struts 4, 5 and 6, which are arranged along the three axes of the octahedron, $1 - 1'$, $2 - 2'$, and $3 - 3'$. The upper ends of the compression struts 4, 5 and 6 lie in one plane and the lower ends lie in another plane below the first. The seemingly complex but truly simple form of the octahedral unit will be understood by identifying the faces of the octahedra, the tension elements and the compression struts as follows:

Eight faces of the octahedra:

$$1 - 2 - 3$$
$$1' - 2' - 3'$$
$$1 - 2 - 3'$$
$$1' - 2 - 3$$
$$1 - 2' - 3$$
$$1 - 2' - 3'$$
$$1' - 2 - 3'$$
$$1' - 2' - 3$$

Twelve tension elements:		*Three compression struts:*
$1 - 2$	$1 - 2'$	4
$2 - 3$	$1 - 3'$	5
$3 - 1$	$2 - 3'$	6
$1' - 2'$	$2 - 1'$	
$2' - 3'$	$3 - 1'$	
$3' - 1'$	$3 - 2'$	

From the foregoing tabulation of the truss elements, the student of this disclosure will appreciate the preponderance in tension elements over compression elements and the significant improvement thus obtained in the direction of utilization of the high tensile properties of the improved materials and alloys available today.

In the preferred construction shown, we have a three-dimensional truss component consisting of struts 4, 5 and 6 and flexible edge portions extending between ends of the struts, these being the twelve tension elements as listed above. The struts are comprised of tubular members. The fastenings 7 are secured to selected ends of the struts for connection to selected ends of the struts of similar components in forming a truss. Fastenings 7 are perforated as at 8, Figure 2, and are secured to the struts by tension wire 11 extending through the tubular struts and through selected ones of perforations 8. Wires 11 are stressed in tension, as by means of nuts 12 threaded onto their ends.

The fastenings may be made with flanges 9 in which are arcuate slots 10 for attachment to cladding sheets such as described in my patent aforesaid.

The wire W is attached to the ends of the struts in suitable manner, as by the means shown in Figure 3. Here a collar 13, with attaching flange 14 is secured to each end of the strut as by welding or brazing. Collar 13 is interiorly threaded and castellated to make tapered notches 15. These receive and position wire W as it is spun onto the strut complex. A locking ring 16 with notches 17 for engagement by a wrench is fastened into the end of collar 13 for clamping the wire into engagement with the bases of notches 15 wherever the wire lies. Notice that the wire crosses each end of each strut twice. Fastenings 7 are secured to selected ends of the struts after locking rings 16 have been set. Figure 1 shows a completed truss component with two such fastenings in place, in this instance at the ends of strut 4. Struts 5 and 6 will be secured to similar fastenings initially forming a part of adjacent components, and struts of adjacent components whose ends are not initially provided with such fastenings will be secured to fastenings 7 of the Figure 1 component as indicated at 4', 11', in Figure 1. The perforations 8 in the fastenings furnish a selective adjustment of the angular relationship between the struts (such as struts 4 and 4') of the interconnected components.

With reference to Figures 4-8, I shall now describe a preferred form of apparatus for spinning the tension wire over the ends of the struts to make a three-dimensional truss component. This apparatus will be described in its particular application to the fabrication of a truss component of octahedral form having its eight triangular faces outlined by the tension wires of the complex. Three struts 4, 5, and 6 extend between the three pairs of vertexes as has been described with reference to Figure 1. The apparatus comprises means for holding the struts 4, 5, and 6 in predetermined angular relation to one another to form a preliminary strut assembly. This means comprises clamping members 18 and 19 fixed to a hub 21 for attachment to shaft 22 of a device for rotating the strut assembly, such as a rotator 23 driven by motor 24. The apparatus further comprises means for feeding a wire W for attachment to the ends of the struts 4, 5, and 6, and means 25 for producing relative movements between the rotating strut assembly and the wire feeding means to bring the wire into engagement with first one strut end and then another, thus to form the flexible edge portions of the truss component.

Relative movements between the rotating strut assembly and wire feeding means are controlled by a "reader" drum 27, Figure 6, in which are stored data for successive relative positions of these parts of the apparatus, and a photoelectric sensor 53, Figure 7, which translates the stored data into controlled operation of the aforesaid relative movements in timed relation to rotation of the strut assembly.

In Figure 4, the strut clamp 18, 19 is shown "exploded," i.e., with member 19 displaced to the right to allow removal of the completed truss component. Grooves 20 in member 19 are disposed in a predetermined angular relationship to one another and cooperate with complementary grooves in member 18 in determining the angular relationship between the several struts. In the particular construction shown, the rotator 23 may turn the strut assembly about the axis of shaft 22 at a constant speed, and will turn three revolutions to spin one octahedron. Reader drum 27 is driven by rotator 23 through a 3:1 chain drive (not shown) so as to turn one revolution to each three revolutions of the rotator. Thus each revolution of drum 27 can direct the movements of the wire guide 25 throughout the spinning of one complete truss component of octahedral form.

Wire leader 25 is capable of moving the guide 28 horizontally and vertically, or both simultaneously. Wire W passes through an aperture 28' in the guide 28 after being fed from a reel. As the wire is fed into the apparatus, it is placed under controlled tension, using for this purpose any of the known devices for tensioning feed wires. Horizontal movement of guide 28 is produced by a reversible motor 29 which is geared to screws 30 and 31, driving lead unit 32 horizontally. Shafts 33 and 34 serve to guide the horizontal movement. Vertical movement of guide 28 is produced by a reversible motor 35 which is geared to screw 36, 37 being a guide rod for such vertical movement. When motor 29 is operated for horizontal movement of guide 28, rod 38 fixed thereto slides through sleeve 39 so as not to produce any movement of the vertical rod 40. During this horizontal movement, wire 41, which is fixed at one end to lead unit 32, is wound or unwound on or from drum 42 fixed to a rotatable shaft which also carries spool 43. The wire 44 and spring 45 move a stylus unit 46 one way or the other to produce a line on the graph paper on drum 27. When vertical movement of guide 28 is produced, shaft 38 acts to raise or lower vertical rod 40 to wind or unwind wire 41' on or from reel 47 which is mounted on a shaft 48 connected to spool 49 on which is wound a wire connected to stylus unit 50 biased by a spring 51. The shaft 48 of spool 49 is hollow, and is concentric with the shaft for spool 43. Stylus 46 records a trace for horizontal movement, and stylus 50 a trace for vertical movement, of guide 28.

When setting up the control pattern on reader drum 27, the rotor motor 24 and leader motors 29 and 35 can be operated by manual switching (not shown) so as to bring the aperture 28' of guide 28 into the proper successive positions to connect the wire W to the respective ends of the struts 4, 5 and 6 as each in turn is presented to the wire leader. Errata and irregularities in the graph on reader drum 27 as produced during this manual pilot operation for a given design of truss unit can be straightened out on the graph by manual editing. Thereafter the area between the two traces may be blacked in as illustrated in Figure 7 to complete the photoelectric playback pattern.

Once the data for the desired design of truss component have been stored in the manner described, stylus frame 52 is removed and the wires 41 and 41' disconnected. If desired, the rods 38 and 40 also may be removed. Then the photoelectric sensor 53 is installed over the drum 27 in the manner shown in Figure 7 to give orders to the leader motors 29 and 35 according to variation of light in the drum pattern. It may be observed at this point that the graph sheet upon which the data are stored is removable so that the spinning program for each different design of truss component can be filed for later use as needed. Thus a program for each design of component, once recorded, need not be re-created. Although I have described one desirable method of programming according to which manual settings are recorded from a prototype setup, it will be understood that other methods of programming are feasible. For example, the programs can be calculated through mathematical or graphic solution, and with the aid of conventional computers as desired.

A playback control for the lead motors 29 and 35 is illustrated in Figure 8. This is a diagram for one of the two photocell and motor hook-ups, here considered to be the one which controls operation of motor 29 for producing horizontal movements of wire guide 28. A photocell P in the sensor 53 provides a voltage between a pair of leads 58 and 59 connected in a bridge circuit 64 containing conventional resistors, as shown, and energized by a source 65 of direct current. The voltage output from photocell P varies in accordance with variations in the outline of the trace defined by the edge of the dark area on the playback drum adjacent the sensor 53. The voltage appearing between contact 66 and lead 67 of the bridge 64 varies in accordance with the horizontal position of the aperture of wire guide 28, Figure 6. Contact 66 may be mounted on the horizontally movable wire lead unit 32, as shown, and has a sliding contact with a resistance wire 68 which is attached to insulator supports on fixed portions of the leader 25. The resistance wire 68 is energized by a direct current source 69, Figure 8, to form a potentiometer.

When the wire guide 28 is located to one side or the other of the desired position as directed by the trace, an unbalance voltage occurs across bridge 64. This unbalance voltage is fed through a pair of leads 70 and 71 into an amplifier. The output from the amplifier is supplied to motor 29 through connections 62 and 63, moving the wire guide 28 toward its desired position as directed by the trace. The direction of the direct current produced in the leads 70 and 71 by the unbalance voltage will be determined in accordance with the position of the wire guide whether to one side or the other of its correct position at any particular moment in the programmed spinning cycle. The motor will thus be operated in a direction determined by the direction of the current produced by the unbalance voltage. When the wire guide reaches its correct position, the bridge becomes balanced, and the voltage across the leads 70, 71 drops to zero, stopping the motor 29.

Similarly, for control of the operation of motor 35 to produce vertical movements of wire guide 28, there is a contact 66′ mounted upon the wire guide 28 so as to follow its vertical movements. Contact 66′ has sliding engagement with a resistance wire 68′ attached to insulator supports on horizontally movable portions of the lead unit 32. Contact 66′ and resistance wire 68′ are included in a vertical control circuit corresponding to that shown in Figure 8. Contact 66′, Figure 6, corresponds to contact 66, and resistance wire 68′ corresponds to resistance wire 68. The output from the vertical control circuit is supplied through connections 62′ and 63′ to the motor 35.

The design of the particular component to be fabricated will determine the form of the clamping members 18, 19, and the disposition of the complementary grooves 20 in such members. A series of different clamp designs may be provided for this purpose or, if desired, the clamps may be made adjustable so that the angular dispositions of the grooves relative to one another can be varied at will. In either case, the means for holding the struts in any one of a number of predetermined angular relations to one another is thus adjustable.

In addition to the means for holding the struts in predetermined angular relation, I have provided means for indexing the relation between the struts to predetermine the relative dispositions of the ends of the struts for a given angular relation. For this purpose, my preferred form of apparatus includes an indexing fixture 54, Figure 4, having recesses 55 to receive the ends of the struts and properly position them within the clamps 18, 19. Either by regulating the relative depths of the recesses 55 in the fixtures 54 or by predetermining the angular disposition of the fixture while the struts are being placed in the clamps, the extent to which each strut projects to one side or the other of the clamp is predetermined. Thus angular disposition is governed by the clamp, and lengthwise position within the clamp is determined by the fixture 54. A series of fixture 54 of differing patterns may be used interchangeably to secure a variety of designs of truss components, each being related to a given set of clamps 18, 19, or to a given adjustment in the case of an adjustable clamp. Alternatively, fixture 54 may be provided with suitable adjusting means for altering the relative positions of the ends of the struts. The positions of the recesses 55 in the fixture may be predetermined by mathematical or graphic solution, or with the use of a computer, as desired. My invention is not concerned with the computation of the form of the truss component, as the apparatus and method can be used regardless of the particular design of component. Following indexing and clamping of the struts, indexing fixture 54 is removed, and the operation of spinning the wire W onto the strut ends can begin.

When using the octahedral form of truss component described and shown, it is possible to spin a wire around the six ends of the criss-crossed struts without reversing the direction of rotation of the strut assembly during the process. One feasible order of accomplishing this is to begin at vertex 2, locking the end of the wire to this vertex, carrying the wire from vertex 2 to vertex 1, thence to vertex 2', etc., according to the following sequence:

Order of spinning:

$$2 - 1$$
$$1 - 2'$$
$$2' - 1'$$
$$1' - 3$$
$$3 - 1$$
$$1 - 3'$$
$$3' - 2$$
$$2 - 3$$
$$3 - 2'$$
$$2' - 3'$$
$$3' - 1'$$
$$1' - 2$$

This order of spinning will be found suitable when the rotator is turned in the direction of the arrows shown around the shaft 22 in figures 4 and 6. A reverse order might be followed. As another order of spinning well suited to a regular octahedral unit having eight equilateral triangular faces as represented in the diagram of Figure 9, I may proceed as follows: set up the three struts in the clamp 18, 19; then, instead of rotating about the axis of hub 21 (Figure 4), set up the strut 1 − 1′ in arbors for rotation about the axis of strut 1 − 1′ and spin in the order:

$$2 - 3$$
$$3 - 2'$$
$$2' - 3'$$
$$3' - 2$$

Then set up with strut 2 − 2′ in arbors and, rotating about axis 2 − 2′, spin:

$$1 - 3$$
$$3 - 1'$$
$$1' - 3'$$
$$3' - 1$$

Finally, place strut 3 − 3′ in the arbors and spin:

$$1 - 2'$$
$$2' - 1'$$
$$1' - 2$$
$$2 - 1$$

This method will also work for spinning irregular octahedral units so long as the wire feed is moved to and fro in the manner described above. It will be appreciated, however, that in the case of the regular, or substantially regular, octahedral unit the movements and apparatus can be simplified for the reason that the step of producing relative movements between the rotating strut assembly and the wire feed can be performed by rotating the strut assembly without appreciable movement of the wire feed, if any.

106

I call attention to the fact that the wire leader 25 comprises means for moving the wire guide 28 to and fro in different directions of linear movement to produce two-dimensional movements of the guide, the control means serving to control such two-dimensional movements of the wire guide in timed relation to rotation of the strut assembly to produce the three-dimensional components. Movements of the wire guide 28 are not necessarily restricted to the horizontal and vertical as shown in Figure 6, as it will be appreciated that the wire feed can be disposed in any position relative to the rotating strut assembly which will serve to bring the guide 28 into proximity with each strut end successively.

After completion of spinning, and the application of the locking rings or collars 16, Figure 3, clamp 18, 19 is opened and the truss component will be self supporting. If desired, spacer member 56, Figure 5, may be inserted between the criss-crossed portions of the struts and a tie 57 applied around the struts and spacer.

EPILOGUE

IN one of his "extraordinary moments of purely poetical lucidities," Fuller has ventured boldly into the unknown could-be's of the future:

With major dimensional expansion in unimpeded environment controls, which are automatically self-erected in remote, rocket ferry-reached, installation locales, it may well be practical, and possible, to install within giant Tensegrities all the component phenomena which enter into the regenerative cycles of complementary chemical event patterning governing local exchange balancing of oxygen and carbon molecules alternately favorable to respective metabolic environments of animals and vegetables.

A Tensegrity sphere, suitably skinned, may be capsule-folded for rocket-borne release outside of earth's envelope with automated opening. So that, if still within Earth's gravitational domain, it would return to the atmospheric envelope as a Ping-Pong ball thrown upon the ocean, decelerating in approximately frictionless subsidence to exquisite equilibrium, to float around the outer atmospheric surface, as a ship upon the sea, gradually leaking and submerging only if its skin sieve mesh is not everywhere smaller than the air molecules. If such a Tensegrity is of adequate magnitude, it can be ballasted, contain importantly large man activities and apparatus, and be rocket-propelled in directional control for progressive positioning. It can contain a small 100 ft. Tensegrity, in turn having an air concentration tolerable to man, without important altitude loss.*

Such is the vision of a heavenly body created by man himself—a hollow Tensegrity sphere floating sublimely upon earth's atmospheric ocean as revealed to the mind's eye of Richard Buckminster Fuller, much as once upon a time there was revealed to Jules Verne the vision of man flying within that atmospheric ocean in poetic

"Argosies of magic sails,
Flying down with costly bales."

Fuller here reveals the power of comprehensive, searching analysis as, with careful attention to the applicable scientific considerations, he extrapolates from his established Tensegrity discoveries. Having harnessed tensile force to better purpose for life in Earth's lands and seas, he now foretells how tensile integrity structures may one day provide a life for man beyond the skies.

---

*Foreseen by Fuller as early as 1960. Portfolio & Art News Annual, No. 4, 1961